SCHIZOPHRENIA: VOICES IN THE DARK

THE CARE SERIES

Schizophrenia: Voices in the Dark

Hope For Those Who Care

**MARY MOATE AND
DR DAVID ENOCH**

SERIES EDITOR
REVD DR NIGEL M DE S CAMERON

KINGSWAY PUBLICATIONS
EASTBOURNE

British Library Cataloguing in Publication Data

Moate, Mary
    Schizophrenia: voices in the dark: hope for those who
    care. — (Care series)
    1. Schizophrenics. care
    I. Title   II. Enoch, David   III. Series
    362.26

    ISBN 0-86065-778-7

Printed in Great Britain for
KINGSWAY PUBLICATIONS LTD
Lottbridge Drove, Eastbourne, E. Sussex BN23 6NT by
Clays Ltd, St Ives plc
Typeset by Nuprint Ltd, Harpenden, Herts AL5 4SE.

In loving memory of Philip

Contents

Acknowledgements

Many kind friends and family have given much support while I wrote, and to them I am deeply grateful. My special thanks go to Marjorie Swindley who spent many long hours, not only typing the manuscript, but rectifying my numerous errors. Her enthusiasm and encouragement were also of particular help. It was she who urged me on when the going was difficult and painful.

My grateful thanks go also to Eileen Bairstow, Margaret Burnett and Margaret Short who gave me so much loving help and support not only at the time of Philip's illness and eventual death, but also long afterwards. Special mention must also be made of Captain Robin McIntosh of The Salvation Army, whose prayerful support and comfort was appreciated by each of us as a family.

To Dr T S Cheah, consultant child psychiatrist, my grateful thanks for her help, kindness, support, true professionalism and care—not only during Philip's illness but to myself long after his death.

To Carol and Iain, my children, who in their own particular way gave their love and support.

Finally to my dear husband John for his love and patience, and for encouraging me from the outset that I must pursue my deep conviction to write this book as a loving tribute to Philip, and so that others also may be helped.

Mary Moate

Behind our efforts lies the friendly encouragement and wise counsel of Elizabeth Gibson, Managing Editor of Kingsway.

I wish to thank Mrs Carol Williams and Miss L Mayne for their patient secretarial assistance. Above all I must thank the patients and their relatives who had sufficient trust to allow me to manage and treat them for the last thirty-five years. Without them these words would be merely academic facts.

David Enoch

Introduction to the Series

All around us, Christians are waking up to their responsibility to *care*—for one another, and for all their neighbours in God's world. The old 'social gospel' has been discredited. It tried to rewrite the message and mission of the church as a social and political programme. Many evangelical Christians responded by retreating into a pietism which denied, in effect, that the gospel had social and political implications at all. But more and more they are being called back to their historic role as the heirs of Wilberforce and Shaftesbury. With a fresh confidence in its biblical mandate, the evangelical conscience has reawakened from its fearful slumbers.

Around twenty years ago, two historic developments marked the beginnings of this decisive move towards the recovery of our evangelical heritage. One was the establishment by the Evangelical Alliance of TEAR Fund, to channel evangelical care to needy people overseas. The other was the setting up of the nationwide Festival of Light—now known as CARE (Christian Action, Research and Education)—to channel evangelical concern for the nation. CARE expressed Christian concern through both practical caring initiatives and public, political campaigning.

The roots of CARE's understanding of its mission lie in our stewardship of God's world (which stems from our creation) and our obligations of neighbour-love (underlined anew in Jesus Christ). We have no option but to care for others; and there are two ways in which we may do so—by practical caring for those round about us, and by campaigning for the defence and enhancement of the Christian values of the nation.

This *CARE series* spans these twin concerns. Some books address major public questions, which may be highly controversial. Others focus on practical issues of Christian caring. We pray that this series will help many Christians think through our obligation to be 'salt and light' in society, as loving neighbours and responsible stewards.

NIGEL M DE S CAMERON

Part I

Joy in the Morning

'Weeping may endure for the night,
but joy cometh in the morning.'

(Psalm 30:5)

In spite of the discovery of the 'wonder' drugs in the mid 1950s which successfully remove the main symptoms such as delusions and hallucinations in most cases, schizophrenia remains a major medical and social problem. It is a common disease, and one in a hundred of the population stands a lifetime risk of developing it. While it is no respecter of class, creed or colour, it usually manifests itself among young people in their teens or early twenties.

Mary Moate's account of her young son Philip's illness (in this the first half of the book) constitutes a remarkable case history of a schizophrenic breakdown. It is a painful and moving record which reveals the great suffering of both victim and carer with the utmost clarity and poignancy. But it is also a record of hope.

Mary Moate's account then allows us (in the second half of the book) to deal in depth and detail with the illness in its various aspects such as diagnosis, causation, symptoms, treatment and management. Our aim is to make known the facts about schizophrenia and thus remove ignorance and fear. In turn we trust the knowledge will lead to greater understanding, sympathy and support for this sadly neglected group in our society. If such caring develops it will be sufficient reward for Mrs Moate's courage in writing her account.

David Enoch

1

Arrival

Where do I start to write the story of our son's life? An obvious answer might be 'from the day on which he was born', but this story can't start quite at the beginning, because our son was actually six weeks old when he became ours. Even though the intervening years seem to have passed very quickly, I shall always remember the day he truly became our own. Many events led up to that day—times of sadness and times of elation—and I need to recount some of them so that the rest of our son's story will come into clearer focus.

First of all came the heartbreak, months earlier. Heartbreak is not too strong a term to describe the feeling we experienced when we learned, after undergoing many tests, that we would never be able to have children of our own. This news came as a great shock to both of us. John and I felt almost as though we had been struck a heavy physical blow! At first we couldn't believe the news; it seemed unreal, as though it wasn't happening to us.

This feeling of disbelief lasted for a time, during which we experienced both grief and despair. Surely, most if not all young married couples make plans, have dreams and hopes of what the future will hold for them! We were no exception, and children were very definitely included in those dreams and plans. I have learned since those early naive days, however, that what we plan for the future in our own minds is not necessarily what will actually materialise. And so, when one of those longed-for plans did crumble, we found the reality of our situation very difficult to accept.

The weeks which followed our discovery that we would not be able to have children of our own were a trying time for us. I remember feeling devastated, and somehow cheated. We asked the same question then which we were to ask years later under different circumstances. *Why us?* I felt bitterly resentful. It seemed so unfair. After all, we had a comfortable home, were reasonably well-off, and—most of all—we loved each other very much. Why could not an expression of that love be realised by a child of our own? WHY? This question repeated itself in my mind over and over again, and as if to remind me, I would feel even worse when other young couples around us were having their babies. I couldn't help feeling jealous, which only upset me more. Also, what hurt very much was that there seemed to be an unusual abundance of babies being christened on a succession of Sunday mornings at the church we attended, the Salvation Army. (Both John and I were lifelong members of the Army.)

Here I was, in a confused, angry state, feeling emotions Christians 'shouldn't' feel: resentful and jealous of others, but at the same time hurting inside. Again, little did I realise then that I had every right to feel as I did, upset and deeply hurt. That I was a Christian didn't alter the fact that I was also human and naturally felt normal human emotions.

I needed time to get over my hurt; both my husband and I needed time. There is so much truth in the old cliché that time is a great healer.

For several weeks the hurt feelings, the doubts as to 'why us?', hovered over me like a dark cloud in an overcast sky; but eventually the feelings began to subside. As the pain gently eased itself from me, I eventually accepted the situation as it was. We began gradually to consider the possibility of adoption. This was merely an idea to us initially; but as the weeks passed, the idea developed. It became more and more obvious to us that maybe adoption was the answer to our problem. And so, having finally reached a mutual decision to adopt, God willing, we began to make the necessary enquiries and wrote off to a Christian adoption society based in London.

We were pleasantly surprised to receive a prompt response to our letter of application, saying that, subject to investigations, we might be considered as adoptive parents. This reply really raised our hopes. Surely we would stand a good chance! We felt we could allow ourselves to be optimistic.

Several procedures and enquiries followed in the ensuing weeks to ascertain whether we were to be accepted or rejected as adoptive parents. There was an interview to attend in London, with many questions to answer and medical examinations. All these we had to accept as being essential, and we felt the inconvenience well worth-while if the end result was to be a baby we could call our own.

Weeks passed before we received the longed-for letter saying 'Yes!' We had been accepted as suitable adoptive parents. We were to be placed on a waiting-list until the time came when a baby was available for us. At last the wheels were in motion, and it was now only a matter of time.

I believed then, as I do to this day, that God moves in a mysterious way. Indeed, God was to direct our paths along many routes and diversions which we could never have imagined. Without a doubt, this was one of the first paths along which he was to lead us to our son. I remember how overjoyed we felt at the news of our acceptance by the society. We could scarcely contain ourselves; we told all our close friends and family the news so that they could share in our joy. All we had to do now was to sit tight and wait (we were told) for six to twelve weeks.

How those weeks seemed to drag by! Still, we were

sustained by the realisation that we were not just waiting for
'something', but for a very special little 'someone'. At last,
the longed-for letter arrived from the adoption society.

> We know this letter will fill your hearts with joy when
> we tell you we have a baby boy, aged six weeks, who
> we feel God would have us offer to you.

At *last* the day had arrived, as we had been promised. A
little baby boy was waiting some three-hundred miles away;
he was to be 'our son'. I wept—tears of joy. The letter told
us where and when we should go to see the baby and bring
him home with us.

Though the adoption society was based in London, we
were to travel to Bournemouth to their mother-and-baby
home. We were given directions to exactly where the home
was situated on the outskirts of Bournemouth; and so, a few
days later, we set off on our journey (or perhaps more
appropriately, our pilgrimage)—for this was no ordinary
journey!

We planned to travel almost into Bournemouth, stay
overnight somewhere, and then make our way to the
mother-and-baby home the following morning. And so,
feeling quite optimistic that things would go according to
plan, we set off on our journey into the unknown. We felt
happy as we started out—a little apprehensive perhaps—but
happy nevertheless. We had much to talk about during the
long journey stretching before us.

It was evening when we finally came within sight of
Bournemouth. What a feeling of relief! By this time we were
quite exhausted; we needed a good night's sleep to refresh us
for the following day—and, of course, for the journey back
home again.

At last the day arrived for which we had waited all those
past long months. Awaking quite early that morning, we felt
excited and nervous. Our hopes and aspirations of the past
months were soon to be realised.

Our appointment had been made for ten o'clock that morning, so shortly after breakfast we made our way over the last few miles to the home. I still remember clearly the large old house, set in beautiful grounds, and surrounded by neat flower-beds and lawns.

We were greeted at the door by one of the home's officials, who led us into a large sitting-room, where we waited, chatting informally for a few minutes. There were a few final details concerning the adoption which were explained to us before we were left alone in the room. At last! Here was the very moment—we were about to meet our baby 'face to face' for the first time! John and I sat in silence, awaiting the lady's return.

Almost immediately she re-entered the room, carrying our son in her arms. I find great difficulty in expressing in words the welter of emotions I experienced as she gently placed him in my arms. Suffice it to say that as I looked into the tiny face of that dear little boy, and as I held him close to me, all the heartache, sadness and hurt of those months of waiting faded from me. Here was a tiny person who until then was a total stranger to us, yet whose life, from that moment on, was to be entwined with ours. It was, we believed, by God's divine providence that we had been brought to this place, the three of us meeting at last: a little boy, a helpless, tiny infant, waiting for us to give our love to him; and we, longing to give him our love, to make him our very own son. Yes! Those were rare moments of great tenderness and love, divine moments to cherish and hold dear in our memory.

Nowadays, the importance of 'bonding' is strongly emphasised. As soon as possible following a baby's birth, it should be placed at its mother's breast. We know now that this moment is beneficial for both mother and baby, almost an essential foundation for a happy future relationship between them. Yet, although I had not myself given birth to this child, there was nevertheless a powerful 'bonding' experience between us. I knew this baby was in truth ours. He was *OUR* son.

The following words were given to me a short time later. I have grown fond of them, and they have come into my mind on more than one occasion. Simple words, but with a profound meaning:

> Not flesh of my flesh, nor bone of my bone,
> But still, miraculously my own.
> Never forget for a single minute,
> You didn't grow *under* my heart—but *in* it.
> *(Author Unknown)*

We were left on our own with our little boy, to have a few quiet minutes together, to hold him, to touch his face, to hold his little hands.

This was to be a time of decision for us, for we were left in no doubt that despite misgivings (which are quite natural in such circumstances), nothing would jeopardise our dedication to the welfare of this child in the future. We both believed that he was the 'right baby for us'; that he had been chosen by God to be 'our' son. I believed then, as now, that nothing happens in this life just by chance, but that God himself holds our destiny in his hands. This was not happening by mere coincidence, or by fate, but was God's will for our lives. Thus, when we were asked whether we had reached a decision, we both made it clear that it was our dearest wish to take our baby home with us.

Several hours and many miles later we reached Hull. Never had home seemed more welcoming than it did that day. At last, John and I and our son had arrived—*HOME!*

How quickly those first weeks passed. Our baby quickly settled and became so much a part of us that it was hard to imagine what life had been like before he came into our lives. Watching him develop during those early baby days brought us great joy. However, we were not quite at ease during those first months, because several months had to pass before the baby could legally become ours. A date for the court hearing had been set for early November, and we were very thankful when this date had passed, for we now had the peace of mind of knowing that the 'law of the land' had officially declared this special little boy to be our son. We were also in possession of a legal document saying so. There it was! Signed, sealed, and settled! He was ours, and could never be taken from us.

Our relatives and friends were as relieved as we were that the baby was now officially ours; everyone readily shared in our happiness. Now the event for which we had been eagerly waiting those past months could take place; and on the following Sunday morning, we had our baby christened. Of all the Salvation Army's ceremonies, I personally consider a christening (or 'Dedication Service', the term used in the Army) to be one of the most moving. The purpose of this important occasion is not merely to give the baby its Christian names, but is a public acknowledgment by the parents that they wish the infant to be dedicated back to God for his blessing, whose gift the child is to them. This was exactly what we wished for our son in that simple yet lovely ceremony. We had chosen his name many months previously. That morning he was christened 'Philip John'.

How quickly those early months passed! Philip's first birthday arrived before we hardly realised it. A baby's first birthday must surely be the most important of all, if not for the little one, certainly for the parents. We were no exception, and enjoyed ourselves tremendously. We had bought a little push-along truck containing building bricks for Philip. He took great delight in walking along, holding tightly onto its handle, so proud of himself that he was mastering his first steps.

2

On the Move

Shortly after his first birthday, he took his first steps unaided. We looked on with pride as he gained confidence with every step. Now there really *was* no holding him back. Philip was on the move. Several months later, in fact, we were *all* on the move—quite literally.

A move had become necessary because my husband, John, was furthering his musical career. A vacancy had arisen in the BBC Scottish Symphony Orchestra, based in Glasgow. Much to our delight, John's application for this post was successful. He was to be appointed a member of this orchestra. In many respects it seemed strange that faraway Glasgow was the place to which we were to move. I must say, the thought did occur to me, 'why Glasgow?' Only later did we come to appreciate that this was yet another development in God's plan for our lives.

In early February 1970 the time came for us to make the actual move. Of all the months in the year, February must surely be the worst of all to move. To say that it was cold is an understatement! On the day we moved, the temperature fell below freezing-point, and Glasgow felt more like the Antarctic than Scotland. As we shivered our way through that day, I must confess I wondered if we had made a mistake. Here we were in a strange city among strangers. I felt very homesick at first. (Who wouldn't?) We had much to do, however, to get settled in our new home, and little time for regrets.

Although it took us a while, we eventually settled in our new home, and in the new surroundings. Gradually we made friends. We discovered that our neighbours— although a little reserved at first—were nevertheless warm and kind-hearted people, once the ice was broken. We loved them. I found the quick Scottish wit and sense of humour very appealing, and a delight in conversation.

We made friends too in our new neighbourhood, for— like us—they were generally young married couples with small children. This meant that Philip had little playmates with whom he could make friends. Out in the garden or in and out of the house, he played happily with our neighbours' children and loved to be with them. Indeed, he was a happy little boy; life at that age was a great adventure to him—a time of exploration. He had boundless energy and was always on the go.

He and his little pals frequently got into mischief. I well remember the day when three of them decided to have a 'wee competition' in a puddle, to see which of them could aim the furthest. (I seem to recall Philip being the winner!) Two of us happened to spot them in the act. We found it a little difficult, trying to explain to small boys that this was not quite the 'done thing', for theirs was the age of sweet innocence, when anything seemed allright. We had to smile to ourselves! I remember, too, the time when Philip had eaten more than his share of chocolate biscuits. When I discovered this and was irritated with him, he said (with a cheeky, innocent look on his face), 'But Teddy's eaten them!' These and other moments come back to my mind as freshly as when they first happened: a source of amusement at the time, now treasured memories.

Many months had now passed since our move to Glasgow. We now felt quite settled, and considered it to be our home. Meanwhile, we had often discussed the possibility of adopting another baby when Philip reached between two and three years of age. We both wanted another, so we decided to write once more to the adoption society in London. The situation had however changed considerably since we had adopted Philip. The society replied saying that, sadly, the waiting list was temporarily closed: there was now an acute shortage of babies available for adoption.

We felt somewhat disappointed, but nevertheless decided to pursue the matter nearer home. We began to make enquiries locally, starting with the local authorities. The outcome of our application was, much to our delight, that we were accepted. Again there were as many questions to answer as before we adopted Philip. We understood the need for these careful checks and began the familiar routine again.

One question—one very important question—was put to us. Had we any preference for a boy or a girl? We had already given this much thought. John and I both felt it would be lovely to have a baby daughter to make our family complete. Yet we would not be disappointed if we were to have another little son. After all (we reasoned) had we had children of our own, we wouldn't have been able to choose.

After the preliminary enquiries were completed, and we learned that we were on the waiting list, we relaxed and got on with everyday life. We expected a long wait and assumed we would be waiting months, not weeks.

A telephone call, quite out of the blue one day, therefore came as a great surprise only a few weeks after our application had been accepted. I remember the day well. John answered the 'phone to hear the social worker telling us that *twins* were available, a boy and girl, and that they thought they should offer them to us. Apparently the local authorities had held a case conference, and our names had been put forward as suitable adoptive parents for the babies.

The social worker made it very clear to us that they did not expect an immediate answer, for they appreciated that it would take time for us to decide. We certainly didn't make a hasty decision; we thought the matter through very carefully indeed, wanting to be sure that the decision was right for us.

However, happily, we both reached the same conclusion—that we *would* take the twins. It seemed such a natural thing to do. Indeed, the more we thought about it, the more convinced we became that these babies were meant to be ours. We had felt the same assurance and certainty two years before when Philip become our son. We firmly believed that this was God's plan for us.

We were completely at peace with our decision, and the twins became part of our family in seemingly no time at all. We loved them both dearly from the moment they first came to us. They were beautiful babies, with sweet, sunny little personalities, even as small babies. And once again we were relieved when the legal proceedings were all finalised. Now our family was complete with Philip and the twins, Carol and Iain.

Once again, as well, those early weeks and months flew by! Life was quite hectic, and packed with washing and feeding times. Soon Carol and Iain were toddling around; then we *really* had our hands full, for they were both mischievous and inquisitive, and there was seldom a dull moment.

Philip, meanwhile, was also quite a handful. He too was a happy, chattering little boy. He had boundless energy and was at his happiest when he was free to release it. From an early stage, he always appeared to be older than he actually was. For instance, when he was two, he looked three; and when three, could be mistaken for four. At times, we had to be aware of this and remember not to expect too much of him; to make allowances for him—because although he looked older and taller than his years, he actually behaved quite typically for his age. This caused some slight misunderstandings at times, with folk outside the family—but nothing untoward. Philip himself was blithely unaware of his height, and his early childhood was happy and carefree, as every childhood should be. Sometimes he of course got into rough-and-tumbles with his friends. Scraps and scrapes were all part of normal life for him.

I remember having a real fright one day when Philip was about three. He was playing in the garden, as he loved to do, but after a little while I realised he had disappeared! I began to search for him in various places where I thought he was likely to be, but there was no sign of him. Eventually I telephoned the police, worried by that time that something dreadful had happened to him. Sure enough, they told me that he had been taken to the police station by a woman who had found him wandering into the village, not far away, on his own. When I arrived, quite distraught, I found him sitting in the police station, chatting away to one of the officers and eating a piece of chocolate cake a policeman had given him. He greeted me with a broad smile, utterly unconcerned by it all. I wept with relief that no harm had come to him!

Shortly after that incident, Philip started going to a play-group, much to his delight (and mine also, I might add). For a few hours each morning, he was happily playing, and learning at the same time, along with other children of his own age. At times this was to prove a source of both concern and amusement, for on more than one occasion Philip fell fast asleep on the private bus that brought the children home each lunch-time. On those days he didn't get off with the other children, but would be found later by the driver on the back seat still fast asleep, quite exhausted after the morning's activities.

Though we very much enjoyed the two-and-a-half-years we spent in Scotland, we never intended to stay for good. One reason was that we lived quite a long distance from our relatives, in particular from our parents, who were now getting on in years, and whom we were unable to see very often. With this in mind, it seemed an appropriate time for

John to apply for a transfer, which was advertised within the BBC, a position in the Northern Symphony Orchestra (as it was then named), which was based in Manchester.

After John's application, the BBC reached a decision rather quickly, and John was given the news that he was to be transferred to the BBC Northern Symphony Orchestra in Manchester. Inevitably this meant another upheaval for us; and this time, of course, we were two plus three!

Within a matter of weeks, however, we found ourselves adapting to a new life in Manchester. We were thankful our move from Glasgow had gone smoothly, and again the first few months of settling in passed quickly. September arrived, and with it Philip's first school-days. To some children, the thought of starting school no doubt brings a feeling of anxiety and even fear, but his attendance at playgroups had prepared Philip well for school, which held no fears for him. In fact he looked forward to the experience with great eagerness.

I remember those first days of school vividly! How Philip enjoyed himself, and loved it all. Each day, when he arrived home, he would tell us with great excitement what he had been doing. The sand-pit held a particular fascination for him. Play is known to be a most important and essential part of education for a young child, and we saw this clearly in Philip's case. Later, when there had to be less time spent on play, and more on lessons, Philip found the routines harder to accept, though he wasn't really upset by them.

While Philip was happy at school, like most children he was equally happy when school holidays came around. One occasional treat, to which he really looked forward during the summer holidays, was to spend a few days on his own at Grandma's and Grandad's house (John's parents), who lived at Bridlington, on the East coast. Philip was devoted to them, and likewise they to him. Nothing pleased him more than to be able to spend warm summer days on the beach, digging happily in the sand, making sand-castles and collecting pebbles. Philip loved the sea and the sand. (John and I have bright memories of holidays by the sea when the children were young; for many years we all spent at least part of our summer holidays there.)

Often we would also go farther along the coast from Bridlington to a picturesque spot called Flamborough Head. Through time, the sea has carved little bays in the headland, with caves and chalk-rock pillars. It is a truly beautiful, tranquil place; an ideal place, too, for children to go exploring the caves. Philip in particular revelled in it all, searching into the nooks and crannies of the caves, looking for various pebbles and sea-shells, some of which he would bring home with him. He kept these for quite some time.

When he was young, Philip's hobby (like that of many children) was collecting such things as coins and stamps. These he would carefully keep in a drawer in his bedroom. They were his prized possessions, and from time to time he would bring them out for us to have a look.

As I tell Philip's story, I don't want to give the impression that he was a quiet boy, one who liked subdued activities. Nothing could be further from the truth! On the contrary, he had a robust, boisterous nature, always full of energy, never walking when he could run. And, like many boys, he could at times show aggression; but he also had an affectionate, tender side to his nature, which showed quite clearly sometimes.

Once, when he was young, he found a little bird in our garden which had been injured. Gently he picked it up and placed it in a box, trying hard to make it comfortable in the hope that it would recover. Unfortunately, a short while later, he discovered that the bird had died. But Philip didn't leave his caring at that, asking if he could take the bird to school and bury it there. His teacher told me later that the children in the class held a burial service for the bird. Perhaps, through that incident, the children learned something that day—that death is a fact of life, even for a tiny bird. Philip was satisfied, and the incident quickly passed.

Early in 1974 John's career took yet another unexpected turn, this time in a direction we could never have imagined. He learned that the Timpanist with the Hallé Orchestra was taking early retirement due to ill-health. John's great ambition was that one day he would become a timpanist with a famous orchestra, and while he thought that this ambition would be difficult to achieve, he believed it not entirely impossible. It came as a tremendous, happy surprise, therefore, that his application to join the Hallé proved successful; after an inevitable waiting period, the news came that he had been accepted.

Things moved rather swiftly from then on, and within several weeks John was established in the orchestra. On the face of it, John's may appear to be a glamorous and exciting life (which, without a doubt, it sometimes is), but it does have its disadvantages, and family life inevitably suffers at times. John's absences on tour were a much greater hardship at first, when the children were very young. There were often other engagements away from home, for which he would try to compensate by spending a lot of his free time with the children whenever possible.

We recognized that there was, at times, jealousy between the three children. We didn't look upon this so much as a problem, but as a normal part of childhood, even if, at times, it spilled over into an all-out fight between them. John and I discovered that jealousy is much less of a problem if it *is* recognised and accepted as a normal part of childhood; it is fatal to 'bury' the issue and pretend it doesn't exist.

We were concerned that Philip shouldn't feel 'one on his own' because Carol and Iain were twins, and to help prevent this, John would spend special times with him—just the two of them together. Philip really relished those times. It was a treat for him to go off with John to the local park to play football, and it was a good way of releasing Philip's abundant energy, kicking a football in the wide open spaces.

Another activity Philip grew to like very much was swimming. Timid in the water to start with, once he had mastered the art, he could hardly be kept out of the water. His confidence grew as his swimming strength increased, and in this sport too, he expended a great deal of energy.

Yet another pastime (especially during the winter months when playing out of doors wasn't always possible) was modelling aeroplanes and cars. This became quite a consuming hobby for him. He loved 'doing things with his hands', which gave him the opportunity of self-expression. He would feel quite proud of himself as he completed yet another model to add to his collection. In these activities, and indeed in all he did, he was carefree and content. Whether we lived in Hull, Glasgow or Manchester, Philip was growing up a happy child.

3

School

Though Philip was happy at home, one difficulty did persist, and that was with his school work. The problem appeared to be that he was unable to concentrate for very long. We reasoned that this was surely not uncommon in one so young and didn't worry unduly about it. One plus for him was that he was healthy, with a strong constitution. There were the inevitable outbreaks of various illnesses at school—chicken pox, measles, german measles—to name but a few, but Philip somehow escaped them all! It was rewarding to see him growing into such a fine, physically strong boy. And so, despite the few niggling doubts I had about his school work, I felt that the future looked good for him. Philip certainly enjoyed life—that was obvious.

Philip was also capable of showing his affection to both John and me, even as a young boy. Many a time a forceful young arm would be thrown around my neck with great affection, and he would plant a large kiss on my cheek. What mother's heart wouldn't stir at such a gesture? At such times my feelings of anger towards him (when he had misbehaved unduly) would evaporate—for without question, there were moments when Philip was a little terror! But then, he was an ordinary, normal little lad, quite capable of getting up to pranks, exactly like any other boy of his age. His displays of affection were, however, the 'plus' times of being a parent.

Days, weeks, months and years passed by, and 1977 dawned. We had been wondering for some time whether we should again move house, because our home was rather too small for our growing family's needs. It was in October of that year that we finally moved to a larger house on the other side of the city.

The children soon settled into their new schools and adapted well to the change. They quickly made friends, not only at school, but at Sunday School also, for soon after we moved, we linked up with the Salvation Army in our new area.

That year, several boys of Philip's age were with him in the Sunday School, one or two of them sharing his same boisterous temperament. Their liveliness made it difficult for those who taught them, and I suspected that on more than one occasion they felt exasperated, to say the least! After all, it was their task to teach the children about God's love for each of them, and also about loving and being tolerant of one another. But there were Sundays when, no doubt, their own tolerance was put very much to the test when the boys argued noisily. Still—they were not looked upon as 'bad' lads, just high-spirited and a bit of a handful. It is ironic that the Salvation Army, formed over a century ago as a body of people to 'fight' the sin and evil in the world and to spread the message of the Lord Jesus Christ to people, had also to nurture boys like our Philip! It appeared, at times, that our young boys took the meaning 'to fight' too literally! However, they were lovable ruffians.

Soon a new man was appointed as Sunday School Superintendent or, as he is known in the Army, 'Young People's Sergeant-Major'. A more suitable person could not have been appointed, for it became obvious very quickly that this man had a calming influence on the children—particularly on the boys! He was affectionately known as 'Uncle

Norman' by the children. How they all loved him, and likewise, he them!

Philip held Uncle Norman in high esteem, often talking about him long after Sunday School was over. Uncle Norman's kindness and caring was on-going, not just reserved for Sundays. On a number of occasions he would invite a few of the children at a time to his home for various activities. I well remember that one Saturday, he collected Philip early in the morning, and took him to his home. Later that day Philip returned, proudly carrying a bird-box he had 'made' under Uncle Norman's supervision. Philip was thrilled with it, and the bird-box took pride of place on the tree in our garden. Sure enough, the following spring, much to our delight, a pair of blue-tits made their nest in it and produced young. Uncle Norman was, without doubt, one person in Philip's life who influenced him deeply for good.

Philip was also very fond of his Grandma and Grandad; they too, left a lasting impression on his young life. Although he did not appear too upset when they died (for he was only eight at the time), I remember that the following year when the cards arrived on his birthday, there was a sadness about him, albeit briefly. Looking at all the cards arranged on the mantelpiece, he quietly commented, 'My card from Grandma and Grandad is missing.' For a fleeting moment he had felt grief at his loss of them, and expressed it poignantly on his birthday.

Soon, of course, he was his usual happy self again, but such moments made us realise that there was a tender side to Philip's nature, even though he was such a boisterous lad of only ten.

Meanwhile, Philip continued to join in activities at the Salvation Army, one of which was cornet lessons. He hoped very much that he would be able to join the boys' band. After quite some time (and a struggle), he did become proficient enough to be in the band along with his friends. John and I were pleased; it was another outlet for him, absorbing his interest as well as his energy.

Philip was still the happy-go-lucky, carefree boy he had always been. True, his boisterous, sometimes aggressive nature caused me some concern, but I told myself on more than one occasion that as he grew into his teens he would settle down and quieten, and that this was only a phase in his life.

The time now approached for Philip to transfer to the comprehensive all-boys' school, an event to which he didn't look forward at all, though he accepted its necessity.

I can remember that first morning he was to attend his new school. When he was ready to leave home, I remarked how smart he looked in his new uniform. Suddenly he became very upset and started to cry. Since it was only on rare occasions that he cried, I immediately sensed that he was feeling apprehensive about what he was to face.

'I don't want to go,' he said. In those few moments, he reached out to me for reassurance, for consolation. I tried to reassure him that there would be many boys that morning who would be feeling scared, exactly as he felt; they too would be wishing that they didn't have to go. This seemed to pacify him, and after a hug at the door, off he went. I was thankful he had been able to express his feelings, not to keep them bottled up before school.

Much to my relief, when he came home later that day, he was in a much happier frame of mind. The new school wasn't so bad after all, he said. In fact, as the first term passed, and then another, Philip eventually settled down at school and enjoyed the first year. We almost forgot that first morning, when he had felt so unhappy, so uncertain. Then the summer holidays were upon us yet again. School could be forgotten (at least for a little while).

When I look back on Philip's childhood with its many incidents—some happy, some unhappy—I realise how

ordinary, normal, and much like any other child's his life
was! I look back and remember Philip: the tiny, beautiful
baby, the inquisitive little toddler, the mischievous boy, then
the older child. And as I reflect on his life, I find I am asking
myself a potent question. Was there anything about his
childhood that I would have changed, had it been in my
power to do so? Answering as honestly as I can, I would give
a very definite 'no'. There would have been nothing about
him I would like to have changed.

I might, however, have tried to change some of my own
attitudes: to accept the loud and boisterous part of Philip's
personality as part of himself. I would not have been so
concerned about how others might have looked on him.
Perhaps, too, I might have been able to say (if only to
myself), when someone who lived across the road com-
plained to Philip one day that he was shouting too loudly,
'So what? Being "loud" is part of Philip's make-up, part of
his own individuality. He is as he is!—as God made him!' I
feel, sadly, that we live in a society which doesn't always
accept the individual as he is, as a person. The term 'live and
let live' doesn't always apply. Instead we are expected to
conform to a specific mould, even to bring up our children
likewise.

What have I learned from mothering Philip? That our
children are God's precious gift to us. And as God is a God
of Love—a God who cares about us individually, and who
longs to pour His goodness upon us—it follows that he
wants us to enjoy our children, to be happy about them,
whatever their personalities might be: whether they be shy,
timid, quiet, or loud and boisterous.

It is comforting to me now, in hindsight, that Philip had a
happy childhood, that *he* was aware of being loved; that we
tried, as best we knew how, to give to Philip of ourselves.
This thought did sustain us later, as time moved on, and
another phase in Philip's life began. He was now growing
into an adolescent!

4

Withdrawal

Adolescence is considered by many to be one of the most painful and difficult periods in a person's life. What with the physical, emotional and hormonal changes taking place all at the same time, it is small wonder that while some pass through this phase with seemingly little difficulty, others may be thrown into turmoil. No doubt the 'emotional growing pains' are the worst for any young person to cope with. He or she can appear to be either arrogant, self-opinionated, boastful, or moody. All these so-called 'negative' expressions of personality and feeling can be present individually, or—worse still—they may all occur at the same time to a greater or lesser degree. An adolescent's behaviour can fluctuate between being quite adult and being utterly childish.

This phase does call for great tolerance and patience from those who care for and live with adolescents, and many adults find adolescents quite irksome! It helps to remember, however, that there remains a little of the child in us all, and, depending upon our situation, this childishness can rise to the surface. It seems quite logical, then, that if we are able to accept this swing of attitudes as a fact, and not feel threatened by it, tolerance comes much more easily, bringing a sense of equilibrium to all concerned. We can begin to learn to 'play it by ear', to give and take, as adults trying to be tolerant, while the youngster learns to accept that adults have feelings, too!

I am reminded here of the important interview John and I had to undergo at the London adoption agency, when we were applying as would-be adoptive parents. One of the many important questions put to us was simply this: would we try to look ahead—not just on a dear little baby, or charming toddler to love—but beyond, to the possibly difficult teenager? Did we feel that we could accept those difficulties, should they arise; and if they did, could we cope? These difficult and unusual questions took us by surprise. I suppose we replied rather glibly at the time, and paid little heed. After all, the situations discussed were years away, and how many couples stop to ask themselves such questions before they take the important step of parenthood?

But here we were, years later, finding ourselves in just such a turmoil, now that Philip had reached his teenage years. It dawned on us that Philip was approaching adolescence when he started to have alternating mood-swings. These were not so noticeable at first. On his good days, Philip was the cheerful, happy lad he had always been. He had a keen sense of humour and fun. He enjoyed a hearty laugh, and we used to hear his loud, irresistible laughter ringing round the house and start smiling ourselves! He had a thoughtful and caring attitude, too, happily taking his share of small tasks around the house.

Philip seemed popular with his friends. One or two lads from the Salvation Army would call for him, and off they would go together, usually on their bikes. At other times he and his friends would stay in his bedroom, listening to pop records, having cups of coffee and sharing fun and laughter together, much as many teenagers do. His bedroom was typical of any teenager, the walls covered with posters of various pop stars or great actors.

As time passed, however, a change came over Philip. He was much less cheerful, and his face began to take on a sullen expression. He seemed to spend more time alone than before. There were times, too, when he showed outbursts of aggression, which were unpleasant for us all. But having listened to other parents with teenagers and observed other youngsters as well; noticing that they could appear sullen on one occasion and quite cheerful on another—we accepted that Philip was merely going through adolescence. We decided that come what may, we mustn't worry ourselves unduly about it. Given time and patience, he would grow through this phase, and be all right at the end of it. After all, mood-swings are not unusual in teenagers; and as they strive from being the dependent child to become the independent adult, they feel a natural need to be alone at times.

Looking at all these points objectively, we were not pessimistic about Philip's future, even if we were concerned for him. In the mean time, all we could do to help was to be there when he needed us, and to show that we did care. (Caring wasn't easy, for he seemed to resent it sometimes.) Still, there *were* good days, when Philip was his cheerful self, and surely—I reasoned—these good days would become more frequent and the bad days less so as Philip's adolescence passed.

Much to our dismay, however, this was not so, for as time went by, events took a turn for the worse. Philip had never found school work easy, and with the extra demands made upon all children in their schoolwork from the age of fourteen onwards, it was becoming clear that Philip's school work was falling off considerably. Yet, despite difficulties, his earlier school reports had indicated that he was trying hard. When Philip appeared to struggle with his work, we tried to encourage him, to urge him on in the belief that if he tried hard, no more could be expected of him.

One afternoon Philip's headmaster telephoned me, saying that Philip had been missing lessons and had left the school without permission and without giving any explanation. Would we try to deal with the matter from our end? That 'phone call left me quite upset and worried. John happened to be working away that day, as he so often did, so I was left to deal with the matter alone. Later that afternoon, when Philip did come home, I tackled him about it. He couldn't really give me any reason why he had walked out of school, though did promise he wouldn't do so again.

I believed Philip when he said this, for whatever he was, Philip was not devious. He would always own up when he had done something he shouldn't, so it did worry us when the episode repeated itself several times during the next weeks. Again the headmaster brought the problem to our attention; although he dealt with Philip firmly, he was a compassionate man, and we talked things over with him several times. His main comment was that from all his many years experience as a teacher and a headmaster (during which he had dealt with truancy on many occasions), he felt that Philip was not truanting in the real sense of the word. (Truants by and large skip school in order to go out and do what they want to do, to have a good time and lark around, but somehow it was different with Philip.) Philip had been spotted quite near the school, completely alone, as though in hiding and afraid to go into the actual building.

John and I both tried hard to help Philip. Often in desperation, we tried to reach him and find out what was making him unhappy, but usually the response was abrupt, and he would say, 'There's nothing wrong.' Sometimes it was actually very difficult to guage his mood—when to talk with him and (we hoped), help him, or when to leave him to be quiet by himself. Over the weeks, I told myself over and over again that Philip would be all right. We just needed more time; eventually the whole unhappy situation would pass.

But try as we did to convince ourselves that the problem would resolve itself and things would return to normal, we grew increasingly aware that we had to face the facts. Philip was not improving, if anything, he was becoming worse.

He began to refuse to see friends who still called on him from time to time. These were the friends whose company he had always enjoyed until then. When I told him that he ought at least to explain to his friends that he didn't want to go out with them for the time being, he would become agitated, even aggressive.

John and I had to make a decision that we could no longer continue to struggle on our own, living from day to day in the hope that Philip would improve. We *had to* seek some professional help.

That help came via our own doctor, who referred Philip to the child guidance clinic for our area. Initially this referral was most difficult for us to accept, for it brought with it a feeling that we had failed somehow, a sense of helplessness—that we must have 'gone wrong' along the way. (Later we discounted these feelings.) Nevertheless, we did know that we had to seek professional help.

The clinical team consisted of a psychiatrist, psychologist, and social workers. During the next weeks and months, Philip was seen by the psychiatrist on several occasions. In spite of her concern and obvious care and compassion, visits proved quite difficult; Philip looked on this help as an intrusion and wasn't always co-operative. Indeed, he was unable to grasp that there was any problem, and this didn't help matters at all. John and I, however, found the clinic's support most beneficial. It was good to be able to *trust* some people, who, while being professional in their approach, did show a real concern for us all as a family. Their caring helped relieve the burden a little.

More than once I asked myself, 'Whatever will become of our boy?' His continual missing of school was still something of a mystery. His progressive, slow withdrawal into himself—not only from us, but from others also—was becoming more of a problem. But *never* did I consider that Philip was deliberately misbehaving. Knowing him so well, I was convinced he would do nothing out of spite or to be awkward. While I had never placed him on a pedestal, nor believed that he could do no wrong, nor that he was perfect, I could *not* believe that my son was behaving intentionally, from choice. I firmly held on to this conviction; nothing and no one could shake my faith in him. I *had* to believe in my son!

If (as I know now) my trust in him wasn't misplaced, then what *was* wrong? The question remained unanswered.

Meanwhile, all we could do was to continue to encourage Philip, to urge him to go out sometimes, instead of always remaining alone in his room, and to get him to attend school. All the encouragement, however, was in itself putting more stress on him. We were caught in an awful dilemma.

In spite of great efforts on our part actually to take Philip to school each morning, it became more and more apparent that he could no longer cope with school. To alleviate the obvious pressure upon Philip, the clinic psychiatrist and the education department decided that he should be taken out of the main school stream for a while, and placed at an education centre especially for youngsters who were having learning difficulties.

Here he responded well. The kindness of the small staff, and the fact that Philip could have more individual attention, proved beneficial. Over the weeks he began to make gradual progress, and really tried hard in his school work. Not once did he refuse to attend the centre, and we became hopeful once again. We appreciated, however, that Philip's placement at the centre was only temporary. What would happen when the time came for him to leave was another matter!

Although he apparently settled down well at the education centre, Philip still remained very quiet and withdrawn on most days, refusing to meet with anyone—neither his own friends, nor any of our friends who called to visit us. On bad days Philip continued to have outbursts of aggressive behaviour, and these become more frequent. The continual strain invariably took its toll. Nerves began to jangle under the continued stress. We became very concerned, too, for Iain and Carol, who were in the middle of it all. It was difficult for them to understand what was happening. Indeed, it was difficult for us all to understand!

We watched helplessly as our son changed from a cheerful, happy, often smiling boy, full of life and vitality, and with such potential; a boy who laughed often, who was capable of giving and receiving love—to a sad, morose-looking, withdrawn boy, with seemingly dwindling energy. He seemed for the most part to reject all our efforts to reach him, although, goodness knows, we tried! (I had doubts even about that. Were we trying too hard? It was quite heartbreaking.)

In spite of all the turmoil, the endless worry and anxiety, we still loved our son. One does not give up loving when difficulties arise. We felt just as much love for him as always. That was the biggest heartbreak of all. We felt that our son, whom we loved dearly, was becoming a stranger to us. All we could do now was to hope and pray, to keep believing, and to look for the proverbial 'silver lining' in what was a very dark cloud in our lives. And, most sadly, in Philip's life.

Over the next weeks we tried to cope as best we could with seemingly never-ending anxiety and worry. If any small signs of hope showed themselves, we clung steadfastly to them in the belief that this nightmare would eventually pass. The fact that Philip continued to attend the education centre each day gave us hope. At least while he was there he *had* to mix with the other youngsters and staff—although (I was told) there were days when he was still very withdrawn.

As Philip's sixteenth birthday drew nearer, there loomed the question of what would happen when the time came for Philip to leave school altogether. Along with the other youngsters at the centre, Philip was interviewed by a careers officer, who was to help him reach a decision about his future. We later realised that this interview had filled Philip with a sense of dread about the future.

During the following weeks, his behaviour changed further. Whereas he had previously been just very withdrawn, now he began to behave rather oddly. We were still encouraging him to go out again with his friends, but he wouldn't hear of it. Then, quite suddenly, he decided to take up running. This was a great idea, which we welcomed at first, but he began to run not just during the day or evening, but into the early hours of the morning!

I discovered this quite by chance. Early one morning I was awakened suddenly by the click of the door. Looking at the clock I realised that it was only 4:30 am. I was puzzled! If Philip wanted to run, why did he choose to do so in the middle of the night, with no-one around? It seemed yet another demonstration of Philip's increasing wish to be alone—completely alone.

He continued to be reclusive. He seemed preoccupied when we tried to engage him in conversation, as if, when we spoke to him, he felt we were intruding into his private world. He even refused to have meals with us as a family, as if he wanted to isolate himself from all of us. This hurt very much, for he seemed to be saying that he wanted nothing more to do with us, a sign, perhaps, of complete rejection. But we wanted Philip to belong. He was *part* of us, part of our family.

We tried everything we knew—encouragement, persuasion, firmness, kindness, love—but seemingly all to no avail. There were times when I felt my patience stretched to the limit, when I felt utterly exhausted. At such times I was so exasperated that I almost felt like shaking Philip; but at other times I felt like holding him to me, in reassurance that he would be all right, just as I used to take him in my arms when he was a small boy in need of a cuddle, or when he had hurt himself. At this time, in fact, he seemed like a child emotionally.

But he was no longer a child physically—he was a young man on the threshold of adulthood. Perhaps (I have thought so many times since) this was part of Philip's problem. He was finding the transition from childhood to manhood too difficult at that particular point in his life. Perhaps he did need *more* time, *more* space! But reasoning was difficult, as it usually is when one is actually living through a situation. We found putting things into perspective also extremely difficult. We fought off disillusionment and hurt, as well. We felt as though all we had tried to do for Philip, all we had tried to give, was being thrown back in our faces. Yes, there was anger too, but against whom that anger was directed, it is difficult to say.

In my confusion I had made half-hearted pleas to God about Philip's true condition, but I somehow felt as though God was not listening. Or, if he was listening, then he was not heeding. Somehow he seemed distant, remote. And so my confusion remained, and Philip's problems remained too.

As this turmoil continued, a nagging doubt hovered in my mind. For quite some time I kept my thoughts and feelings to myself, but this uneasy feeling persisted, and try as I might, the dreaded thought wouldn't go away. I tried to reassure myself, telling myself I was letting my imagination run away with me, that my nagging doubts were due to the great strain we had been under for so long. But despite all my reasoning and self-reassurance, I couldn't help thinking, *Supposing Philip's problem is more than just an identity crisis?* (a term which had been used by the doctor at the clinic), and *Just supposing he doesn't improve? What if it all develops into real mental illness?* This was my worst fear, the state of affairs which I dreaded most, and the nagging fear I had tried to suppress all those past weeks.

Surely—I tried to convince myself—*such a thing could never happen to our son!*

5

Voices

One Saturday morning early in May (in fact it was shortly before Philip's sixteenth birthday), we were all awake except for Philip. I went to his room to call him, and he sat up in bed with a surprised look on his face and said; 'Guess what! I heard voices in the night.'

'Perhaps you had a dream with voices in it,' I suggested.

'Oh no, this wasn't a dream, these were real voices in my mind, speaking to me.' Philip showed no fear of this experience, only sheer amazement and bewilderment.

I suddenly felt sick in my stomach, for it somehow brought my worst dread even closer; what I had most feared now seemed a probability.

Quickly I tried to pull myself together and keep as calm as possible. I tried to persuade Philip that perhaps he had been mistaken after all, that it had just been a dream, and that we all have dreams that seem real. However, Philip remained adamant, believing beyond doubt that he had heard voices. Nothing I could say would convince him otherwise, and during the next few days he would tell me over and over again that he was hearing voices.

Something awful *had* happened to Philip.

I recalled an article I had once read about an illness which very often manifests itself in adolescence. Some of the symptoms described included a gradual withdrawal from other people and from reality, often with delusions and hallucinations, or hearing voices. These symptoms were described under the heading 'Schizophrenia'. I thought through my memories of that article, and about Philip's behaviour over the past months: how he had become gradually more and more distant and withdrawn, not only from us, but from other people too; and now he was *convinced* he was hearing voices! Dreadfully, it all began to fall into place. Surely Philip couldn't be suffering from such a terrible illness as schizophrenia? The very word filled me with horror and fear—for him, and for us. I was FRIGHTENED.

My fear of schizophrenia and its implications was based purely on ignorance, for basically I *was* ignorant at the time about this illness. The very name 'schizophrenia' held for me, then, all sorts of connotations, some of which were quite bizarre, unrealistic and unfounded. In any case, at that point my diagnosis was all supposition. The most important thing now was to get help for Philip—quickly!

In Philip's best interests, the child guidance clinic doctor decided to refer him to an adolescent unit. An appointment was swiftly made. As the day of the appointment approached, we had mixed feelings. On the one hand, we had a sense of relief that Philip was going to have further expert help; but at the same time, we felt great apprehension, a fear of the unknown. We also felt hurt and upset by what was happening to Philip. The clinic doctor had given us prior warning that Philip would probably be admitted to enable full investigations to be carried out, and though this was something we had to accept, we found it painful.

Finally the morning of Philip's appointment arrived. The adolescent unit was a building in the grounds of a large mental hospital. The actual unit was at the back of the main hospital.

I remember too clearly our slow ride through those grounds. An air of gloom seemed to hang over it, bleak and uninviting. And then there were the patients, to whom so many people refer as 'inmates' (a strange and harsh term, I feel, as though they are prisoners placed carefully away from society behind those large gates). I looked at those patients that morning as they walked along in the grounds, oh, so slowly: some with their eyes fixed on the ground, others staring straight ahead, and most of them oblivious of the world around them. Some were quite young, others middle-aged, but many were very old, and one assumed they had been there for many years. For them, this place held no fear. This was their home, a sanctuary from the threatening world outside.

Was this happening to us? This terrible scourge called 'mental illness'? Had our son become one of its victims? We could scarcely believe the nightmare we had all endured over the past months. We hardly dared face the painful reality, yet there we were that day, *having* to believe it, having to accept that something was terribly wrong, and that something awful was happening to our son.

Still, if our worst fears were founded, surely this was the place where we would get Philip the help he so desperately needed. This thought, then, offered just a little consolation to us, that in spite of misgivings, in spite of a sense of fear of the unknown, in spite of a dread of what the outcome might be—here, surely, we would find help, understanding and hope.

In the event, we felt disappointed by that first morning's appointment. We answered many of the questions of the young interviewing doctor, even though we felt that many of them were of little relevance to us. Still, he was the expert, and we were 'at his mercy', so to speak. But we did sense a coolness, an air of indifference almost. I must confess that as we left, I still felt as confused as ever. Although it was a warm June day, a sudden chill ran through me as we made our way down the long, slow drive from the hospital grounds.

They did not decide there and then to admit Philip to the unit. This decision instead came a few days later, at his second appointment. In between the two hospital visits, Philip's condition had deteriorated further, and by that time he had become for the most part completely silent, except for when he answered the voices in his mind, to which he would talk and laugh. Seldom would he respond to us in conversation.

To say we found this distressing would be to put it mildly! We were beside ourselves, having to stand back and look on helplessly as Philip's condition appeared to worsen with each day. But in a strange way Philip himself was spared the pain of this, as, for the most part, he was completely in his own world and wasn't aware of just what was happening to him.

During his second appointment at the unit, Philip was admitted. Our feelings were very mixed that day as we left him behind. In one sense we felt relieved that he was to be cared for by professional people, that he was in 'safe hands' and eventually would recover and be well again. We told ourselves that if Philip had had a physical illness, we would have no qualms whatsoever about his entering hospital, and this situation wasn't so very different. Nevertheless, we could not dismiss our feelings of sadness and confusion.

Little visiting time was allowed for parents: in fact, only one evening a week, and at week-ends. The first evening visit following Philip's admission was terribly upsetting. Philip had realised by that time that he would have to stay in the unit for some time. He pleaded with us to let him come home, and trying to reason with him was almost impossible. He couldn't be reasoned with or reassured, and as we left him that night he looked lost, alone and sad. It tore us apart to see him that way; but however bad we felt, we knew we had no choice but to leave him there if he was to be helped.

As we made our way out of the building and walked the long drive to the bus stop (our car had broken down earlier that day), it was raining heavily. John and I huddled together, silently, under an umbrella, each aware of the other's feelings of sadness and bewilderment, but neither of us able to express it—at least, not then. It was neither time nor place to risk sharing our feelings.

In spite of the dreadful ordeal that evening, later visits became a little easier, for Philip did settle down, though only a little. But he always asked, each time we visited him, if he could come home with us. The repeated question made our visits difficult, not only for us, but for Philip—as he became angry each time we had to refuse.

When Philip was first admitted to the adolescent unit we were told that thorough investigations would be carried out during the first two weeks, after which it was expected that Philip's problem would have been identified, and if illness was diagnosed, treatment would then be started.

However, four weeks went by. Still we hadn't been told anything much at all. We both felt that as Philip's parents we should be told exactly what was wrong. John decided to ask one of the doctors outright. We realised, of course, that by asking a direct question, we must be prepared for a direct answer. It wasn't at all easy, but we had to know what was wrong. This, we felt, was our right.

When John approached the same interviewing doctor we had seen before, our worst fears were confirmed. Back came the answer that, yes, in their opinion Philip was suffering from schizophrenia. The doctor was more helpful this time, adding what seemed at the time to be a strange remark! He said that they did not like to use the word 'schizophrenia'. *Why not?* we wondered. *Why the mystery?*

The thought has crossed our mind since, that had John not asked directly, we might never have been told exactly what was wrong. We might never have found out!

It was all so puzzling. Only later did we realise why there was so much reluctance to tell us, since knowing the truth did not lesson our pain. There is no denying, either, that although we had prepared ourselves to face the truth, when we did find out, it came as a devastating blow. Coming to terms with it would, we realised, take time and patience, but at least we now *knew*. Now we were no longer 'in the dark'. We could begin to find out for ourselves just what schizophrenia was, and the mystery surrounding it. One thing was clear to us—that Philip would need all the help, support, and care we were able to give him. He would also need all the professional help available.

Once the medical team had reached the conclusion that Philip was suffering from schizophrenia, they then decided to put him on medication to relieve the worst of the symptoms. We were relieved, for our main concern now was that Philip, having begun medication, would start on the slow road to recovery. The reason for the doctors' reluctance to tell us the nature of Philip's problem now began to become clear; they had to be completely sure of the cause before they could give a diagnosis on such a terrible illness as schizophrenia. Any mistake could have had disastrous results.

We were told that Philip's progress would be carefully monitored; once stabilised, he would be allowed home for week-ends. For the time being, however, he was only allowed to come home on a Saturday and had to return to the unit to sleep. Soon afterwards his home visits were promoted to full week-ends.

Having Philip home again, even for short periods, filled us with a mixture of happiness and sadness. We discovered that schizophrenia not only affects the mind of the sufferer, but his whole personality too. Philip walked around the house as though he were in some strange place, not in his own home. It was as though he were with strangers, not his own family. Even in these relatively early days of his illness we felt a sense of loss: that we had lost a part of our son which would never return!

We kept reminding ourselves that Philip was ill, that it was still early days, and that, with time, the medication would eventually have the desired effect; Philip's condition would improve. We lived in the hope that Philip would be one of the fortunate ones who would make a full recovery, and that he would once again become the happy, carefree lad we knew before this unhappy period of his life had commenced. We had to believe it—we had to try, difficult though it was to look on the positive side. We had to believe, not only for Philip's sake, but for all of us. We couldn't allow this illness to overwhelm and destroy our happy family life together. We found this kind of reasoning possible on some days; but there were other times when we couldn't feel positive at all.

As for Philip himself, it was hard to define exactly how he was feeling. We tried to include him in conversation, talking about anything at all, no matter how trivial, to reach him and somehow to communicate. It was obvious, however, that for the most part he could take in very little of what was happening around him. In one sense, then, Philip was spared the pain of his illness, and this was a blessing. And yet there was at times a deep sadness and loneliness about him which was quite pitiful, and very painful for us to see.

6

Heartache

We had mixed feelings about Philip's stay at the adolescent unit. Obviously, not all the youngsters were there because they had a mental illness. Mostly they were very emotionally disturbed; that soon became clear to us. The nursing staff were varied in their approach to their patients. Some appeared to be caring and enthusiastic about their work, but others appeared to show little interest in what they were supposed to be doing, and indifference in their caring for the young people in their charge. There was a 'laid back' attitude among most of the staff, and we felt a little uneasy about this, for at times they seemed a bit *too* relaxed. We came to the conclusion, however, that perhaps it was meant to be that way in a unit accommodating so many young people with various emotional problems; and that they were simply trying to maintain a calm, relaxed atmosphere.

It was after Philip had been in the unit for a few weeks that a huge problem arose. He had not settled easily in the first place and in fact had hated it; but we had attributed this attitude mainly to his illness, for even at home he had been extremely restless and unsettled, isolating himself from the other youngsters whenever he could. He also hated taking his medication, protesting that the tablets made him feel continually tired. (This unfortunately appears to be one of the side-effects of some of the more powerful drugs.) But the main problem was that Philip began to make his own way home. He would simply step out of the main door (which was locked only at night) and walk to the main road, where he would board a bus to take him to the terminus. He would then walk the remaining three miles to our home. (The total distance Philip would travel from the unit to where we lived was fifteen miles!)

At first, Philip only came home occasionally, usually after we had taken him back after a week-end at home. As time passed, however, he came home more frequently; and eventually he came home several times a week. This became a major problem, for we had to take him back to the hospital immediately, (at the staff's insistence), sometimes very late at night. Both John and I were weary and angry. When asked why he did it, Philip simply said he wanted to be at home. He didn't *have* to stay in hospital, he said; he was all right.

While the hospital was for many of the patients a place of safety, for Philip it was anything but! To him it posed a threat. All he wanted was to be free from what he felt to be an imprisonment. All he *dearly* wanted was to be at home. We felt desperately torn, for we knew that despite Philip's longing to be home, he could not be. He was still much too ill and had to remain in hospital until he was well again.

His return to health, however, seemed to us to be as far away as ever, for by this time Philip was refusing to take his medication too, which resulted in a rapid deterioration in his condition. The staff insisted that they could not make Philip take his tablets against his will, as he was over the age of sixteen. The only way they would have been able to do so was if Philip were put in a 'section' under the Mental Health Act, and the thought of that possibility filled us with dread. (Dr Enoch explains Sectioning on page 133.)

We were all faced with an awful dilemma, and John and I did not know which way to turn for help.

We felt angry because we couldn't understand why the

nursing staff did not keep a more watchful eye on Philip, knowing he had a tendency to get away whenever he could, and knowing, too, the nature of his illness There were very few youngsters in the unit then, so it wasn't as though the staff were overworked.

Then the staff had the idea of taking Philip's shoes away from him to make him 'stay put'. The final straw came one night when Philip made his way home (he had caught the bus and walked the extra three miles home as usual)—but *without his shoes!* We were not at home when he arrived, but a kind neighbour took Philip in, contacted the hospital for us, and had Philip taken back to the unit.

In other circumstances, the incident could have been amusing, but we were not in the least amused; we naturally felt very upset indeed. As far as we were concerned, action had to be taken for Philip's transfer to another hospital nearer home. We could no longer cope with this constant concern for Philip's safety, knowing how confused, bewildered, and homesick he was.

The doctor made arrangements for Philip to be transferred to another hospital near our home. The actual transfer, however, took four days to complete, as a wait was necessary until a bed became available. Those four days were gruelling—a nightmare, in fact—for Philip had deteriorated right back to 'square one', now that he was not on any medication. We felt utterly alone, with nowhere to turn, and with no-one whom we felt able to contact. (It was a week-end.) Clearly John and I had to cope as best we could with one very ill son. During all those four days and nights, Philip only really slept for one full night. He wandered around the house and out into the garden in a manic state, completely lost in his private world of mental torment, turmoil and confusion. It is difficult to put into words our feelings of utter helplessness and despair!

There is a school of thought among a minority of the medical profession which questions the use of drugs in the treatment of schizophrenia. One of the beliefs is that the person termed 'schizophrenic' is merely making a protest against a society to which he feels he cannot belong. It is difficult to understand, however, how anyone would choose to opt out of society in this manner, were he not extremely ill. Perhaps if those who make such a claim had been in our home to witness those four days, they might well rethink their original theory and even change their opinion entirely. Schizophrenia from a clinical, detached, distanced viewpoint is one thing, but we were experiencing it at its very worst—at first hand! Anyone who has lived with or experienced mental illness at such close proximity will realise the full horror of it.

Here was the son we loved, regardless of what was happening to him, and despite the fact that he seemed like a total stranger to us. We had no doubts at all that Philip was desperately ill.

Much to our dismay, what we had always dreaded might happen became necessary. We had lived in the hope that it wouldn't come to his having to be 'sectioned', that this ultimate step might somehow be avoidable. But Philip finally *had* to be admitted into hospital under a section of the Mental Health Act. To put the position more bluntly, Philip was admitted against his will; the decision was completely taken from him, as he was too ill to make a rational choice. The matter was out of our hands, too! We had to be guided and advised by the medical team, and they felt that it was in Philip's best interest, and for his safety, that he have hospital treatment immediately. It was yet another awful incident we had to accept.

On the day of Philip's admission, I could not even find it in myself to visit him! During the previous few days, that impending nightmare had taken its toll. I felt shattered, devastated and physically ill, so John visited Philip alone that evening. The following evening, however, feeling a little better, I summoned the courage to visit Philip. I wanted to see him, no matter what, so I braced myself for the ordeal I knew would be in store.

When we arrived at the hospital, Philip was sitting on his bed, his head bowed, the curtains pulled closely around his bed area. A lump came into my throat as I watched him looking so sad and dejected. He was obviously sedated now, and his mood had changed from 'high' to 'flat'. He was also extremely tired from lack of sleep over those past days of trauma.

We talked for a while, trying to include Philip in conversation, but for the most part he remained silent. During the final few minutes of the visiting hour, however, Philip suddenly turned and said: 'You've had me put in here—this is what you wanted. Go away!' His words hurt us very deeply, not just because he was saying this to us—his parents who loved him—but because, in his confusion, it seemed to me that this is what Philip really believed of us. But if we felt that Philip had rejected us that night, it is almost impossible to imagine what *he* must have been feeling. Needless to say, I came away from his bedside that night in tears, completely shaken and distraught.

Later on as I thought about him, the mental picture of him looking so lost and dejected turned over and over in my mind. His utter sadness and confusion in his belief that we *had* rejected him, as well as that 'lost and alone' look, threw me into a deep turmoil of emotion. I began to question, *really* to question for the first time, why Philip—a young lad who had done no harm to anyone, a boy with a sweet, carefree charm about him before his illness struck, a lovely natured, handsome-looking boy with a ready smile—why should *he* have all this suffering? Why was all this happening to us, as a family? It was difficult to think straight and to keep a sense of proportion in all the confusion. It was even difficult to pray. The solace and strength which I had always believed one can find in prayer seemed to elude me, and I found this hard, especially in such a dark time in our lives. My prayers were focused on one theme: that God, in his love, would make Philip well and take all the suffering and pain from him. All the confusion made it difficult to trust, or to have even a small measure of faith that my prayers would be answered.

I had heard and read from time to time of various people who, in periods of great personal distress and adversity, had remained strong in a deep, unmovable faith. I could not, in all honesty, make such a claim. Indeed, if anything, I felt utter bewilderment. My mind was in chaos from the events of the past weeks and months. It seemed that whenever things had begun to look a little brighter, something else would happen that would send us reeling back to 'square one' again.

When would it end, all this heartache, worry and anxiety? *How much more can we take?* I asked myself. We felt as though we were on the edge of some dark, gaping chasm into which we were about to fall at any moment, and from which it would be impossible to escape, for that is just how black things seemed to me at that time. And yet, somehow, throughout even this ordeal, an inner, persistent awareness kept prompting us to just keep 'holding on'. And we clung to the belief that this dreadful experience through which we were passing would not last for ever.

In a sense, it seemed that our lives had been uprooted and were then in a turmoil, though the inexorable wheels of everyday life had to keep on turning. Events couldn't stand still; somehow we had to carry on as usual. John in particular felt a great strain, for his work with the Hallé continued throughout. On the whole, musicians are considered to be quite tenacious, but John found it hard to carry on with his routine, and to maintain the high standard required of him in his work. Fortunately, the readmission happened during the holiday period, which allowed him a little breathing-space! A holiday that year was, however, out of the question for us.

With the passing of days, Philip appeared to be settling down in the hospital. He had been quietly restarted on medication shortly after his admission, and his condition consequently began to improve.

Philip was in a very busy psychiatric unit with many patients. We were impressed by the staff, who seemed very efficient. They treated Philip with respect, as a person, and while they were firm with him, and watched him closely, they were most caring in their attitude. He responded well, becoming particularly attached to one of the ward sisters. She was a young woman, small in stature (Philip stood head and shoulders above her), and she would jolly Philip along with a firm but kindly manner.

7

Homecoming

The hospital unit was in a very modern, open situation, and although the exits were quite obvious, Philip had never wanted to get away, except on two occasions towards the end of his stay, when he walked out and came home by himself shortly before his discharge. However, although Philip had accepted his hospital stay reasonably well, he still retained the strong desire to be free and to return home for good. This wish he often expressed, and we found it comforting to know that home for Philip was a place where he felt secure and at his happiest—despite the fact that we had been forced to accept the guidance of the medical staff as to when they felt Philip was finally ready for discharge.

That decision came some seven weeks later when the hospital team decided that there was nothing further they could do to aid Philip's recovery, and that he would no longer benefit by being kept as a full-time patient. They felt he would do better now as a day patient, so Philip was transferred yet again to another hospital where there were more facilities for day patient care. The emphasis here was on occupational therapy, which formed a major part of the rehabilitation programme. The idea was that most of the patients would eventually be well enough to leave the hospital altogether and take their place in the community. At least here Philip was a step nearer to being well again.

Meanwhile, as the weeks passed by, the long, hot summer days were coming to an end, and the cooler, welcoming days of autumn approached, a relief following that summer of intense heat. We somehow managed to establish a routine, and tried to adjust back into some form of normality after the trauma through which we had just passed. We were under no illusions! We knew that the road to recovery would be long for Philip and there would, we realised, be a struggle ahead. It wouldn't be easy for any of us, particularly for Philip.

However, with the passing days, there came a gleam of hope. Little shafts of light appeared in what had been an extremely dark path. Any sign of improvement in Philip's condition, no matter how small, raised our hopes. We began to notice for example that he was trying hard to become a part of us once more, a real family member again. Although he wanted sometimes to be completely alone, to our delight he also began to want to have his meals with us, and joined in the family conversations. He also began to make contact with his friends again and arrange to meet one or two of them. Sometimes he would suddenly say that he was going out for a walk, and off he would go for half an hour or so.

We encouraged these various activities whole-heartedly, for these were all signs for the better. This reaching out to others—whether it was to ourselves, to his friends, or whoever—was a definite step in the right direction, a sign that Philip was putting up a fight, showing a spirit of courage and determination in spite of all he had been through. His lovely smile was returning to his face, for whenever Philip smiled, his whole face beamed, showing a large dimple in his left cheek which was a facial feature he had always had, even as a tiny baby. Yes! We were encouraged by Philip's progress, even though it came very slowly, and we tried not to be too worried when he had a particularly bad spell, bearing in mind that these were inevitable on his road to recovery.

The hospital staff were pleased with his steady progress, and his medication was carefully monitored and adjusted to meet his particular needs. Philip was having fortnightly injections, as well as tablets. Yet for all that the hospital staff showed interest and care of Philip's well-being and were kind to him, and for all that he seemed to get on with the other patients, Philip still had a strong urge to be free altogether from hospitals.

It was quite an awesome task each morning, trying to motivate him to get up and prepare to go off to the day hospital, for like many schizophrenia sufferers, Philip lacked inner motivation to do certain things. His medication, too, had an effect on him, making him drowsy and trembly, particularly early in the day. This situation was in such contrast to his earlier years, when he had met each day with vigour and enthusiasm.

His reluctance to go to the hospital was understandable. It did seem sad that a young lad of his age had to face going along to hospital day after day, and this prospect must have daunted him. Also, for the most part, Philip was unable to express his feelings of frustration and annoyance and was forced to bottle up such emotions in himself.

It was difficult to try to urge Philip on, to try to get over to him that eventually he would be well enough not to have to attend the hospital at all, and that it would all be worthwhile when that day arrived. Most of the time, however, it was not easy to reach Philip, for he was still only able to retain a little of what we said to him. Quite often he would seem almost to be in a trance-like state, staring into space, as though far, far away. And then there were the voices. It seemed as though they were never far away, but Philip denied that he could hear them when we asked if they were troubling him. With hindsight, I believe that in denying he could hear them, Philip was trying to put up a brave fight; I'm sure he hoped they would eventually stop.

It was around this time that we realised that the hearing of voices, such a common feature of schizophrenia, was something Philip was going to have to live with. Having asked at the hospital, we were told that, in spite of having regular medication to alleviate their worst symptoms, some patients are never totally free from the voices; they have to come to terms with this phenomenon as part of their lives. This fact concerned us. We asked ourselves if Philip would be able to accept this reality, and how he would be able to come to terms with it once he realised that the voices might well be a permanent feature of his life. For while Philip denied hearing them, we were all well aware of his distress, as he would mutter under his breath in reply to them, turning his head quickly, almost as though they were sitting on his shoulder—those horrible, tantalising, menacing, imaginary voices! To Philip, however, they were anything but imagined. To him they seemed very real, frighteningly so. It was dreadful to see this happening to him. All we could do was to divert his attention to something else, talking to him about anything at all to take his mind off the turmoil he was enduring.

We tried not to worry unduly about the voices. We reminded ourselves repeatedly that it was yet early days, that progress would be slow, but that eventually Philip would improve. It wasn't easy—not by any stretch of the imagination! For one thing, Philip had difficulty in listening to reason. If he asked for something we were unable to give him, he would continue to ask time and time again, not necessarily because he was being awkward, but rather because he seemed unable to retain what we said to him. Often he would seem like an unreasonable, demanding child—as though he had taken a step back in time, in other words that he had regressed. I still hoped, however, that he would work through this stage and subsequently go on to develop in maturity, and become well again.

If this was happening to Philip, if his demanding, manipulative, sometimes difficult-to-tolerate behaviour was indicative of his eventual recovery from his dreadful illness, then we could wait. We could meet him, not just half-way, but we could go all the way—and what a strain it was! We felt it would be worth the wait and the heartache, if the result was that our son would eventually be well again.

Still, life wasn't all gloomy and nasty. There was a 'plus' side too! We noticed some signs of improvement, for in comparison to how he was before his illness (when he was detached from us almost to the point of hating us with a cold indifference), there was now an about-turn. He became affectionate and warm. He showed consideration towards us and became loving in his attitude. It was as though he was making a great effort to reach us, to make up for the lost time.

This became a great source of comfort to us, even though we were well aware that the childlike phase would probably have to pass in his progression towards eventual recovery. The question remained, however—did his childlike behaviour really matter, at that particular time?—for progress would surely be at a pace that was right for Philip.

In any case, Christmas was almost upon us. We thought it best that we keep Christmas 'low key' that year. Despite the fact that Christmas is associated with happiness and a sense of togetherness, the preparation and build-up for Christmas can, even for the most placid and easy-going individuals, be a time of stress and anxiety. Most of us associate stress and anxiety with unhappy periods in our lives; whereas happy events can be stressful too. And since the level of anxiety a schizophrenic can take is very low, we wanted to keep the stress minimal as we prepared for Christmas.

Nevertheless, we had Carol and Iain to consider, too; we didn't want them to miss out. They awaited Christmas with their usual eagnerness, and so did Philip too, for that matter. In fact, we all awaited Christmas Day with happy anticipation. After all (we felt), we had every right to wish a happy time for ourselves. We had all been buffeted about, and we felt bruised in spirit by all we had endured together over the months. Why shouldn't we hope for a happy time, for a respite from all the pain and heartache?

It was Christmas Eve. We reached a unanimous decision that by way of a change the presents would be opened that night, instead of the usual Christmas morning. This present-opening took place with all the delight common to most families. There were the usual 'oooh's' and 'aaah's' as each parcel was carefully opened, and we all went off to bed that night feely very happy indeed.

I well remember that particular Christmas morning! It had started out as a quiet, peaceful day, but towards dinner-time, this peace became disturbed.

Philip was spending some time in his bedroom, when suddenly there was the sound of him shouting. As I approached his bedroom to find out what was wrong, I could hear him calling, 'Go away' in an almost pleading tone.

The voices he had contended with on and off for several months were now apparently back with a vengeance, tormenting him almost to breaking point. I felt a strong urge to rescue him from this torment, although how to do that was another matter! We were all terribly upset. Why, on that day of all days, did he have to endure so much? Would he *ever* have any peace of mind? Would there *ever* be an end to it?

It seemed that in our determination not to allow Philip's illness to spoil any of our happy plans for Christmas, we had somehow forgotten, had underestimated the fact that the symptoms of schizophrenia are no respecter of persons or of special events. The menacing, sickening presence of Philip's illness was never far away, no matter how we tried to dismiss and eradicate it.

After a little while, Philip became calmer again, although a look of bewilderment and sadness remained with him. We did not know what was wrong, and he was unable to tell us. His sadness and bewilderment were ours too, and all of us felt his pain. However, even this sadness passed, and the rest of Christmas and New Year were spent quietly together.

8

Beginnings and Endings

Inevitably, the New Year had brought with it a sense of relief that the old year had drawn to a close. With it, we hoped that all our heartache was behind us now. No matter what we had been through together in the past, we faced the New Year with optimism. We were not so naive, though, as to believe that there wouldn't be times of difficulty ahead.

And so we came to January, 1985. What can be said of this particular month of the year? Many people, once having recovered from the aftermath of the festive season, experience an unwinding, a 'settling'. On the other hand, January can be a time for taking stock, for re-evaluating the events of the past year, and seeing where and how changes can be made. It is a time of fresh beginnings, of new hopes and aspirations.

As for us, we had mixed feelings as the New Year unfolded. We tried to look forward with optimism, believing that the year to come must be better than the last. At the same time we felt a certain trepidation—justified, we believed, in view of all we had been through. In any event, we felt we would try to live the cliché and take each day as it came.

Philip returned to the day hospital after his short Christmas break with us. As had been the case before, he

66

was reluctant to go, and all we could do was once again to urge him on in the hope that time would make it easier for him. One thing was sure: he was still not well enough to be discharged.

His overall progress was more or less as it had been during the days leading up to Christmas. There were times when we felt so pleased at how well Philip appeared to be doing. On these 'good' days, he would be cheerful, lovely, a delight to be with. The rapport between us was heart-warming, as Philip was giving of himself in what we considered was a brave effort on his part to win through. 'I love you, Mum,' he would say with a warm, cheery smile on his face. Often he would grasp my hand as he said it; and sometimes (quite out of the blue) would plant a kiss on my cheek. After all the months of cold, detached silence, these gestures meant so much to me! Yes, we were well aware that for a lad of sixteen to be openly telling his mum that he loved her could have been considered to be 'a bit soppy'. But the important thing was that Philip felt able to express his warmth and affection. It made him happy too—obviously so—that his feelings were accepted. His long months of apparent indifference were fast becoming a fading, unhappy memory.

While there were these good days, when Philip seemed to be much better, there were still the worrying times when he withdrew completely within himself. No matter how we tried to reach him on such occasions, we had little response from him. It was then we became aware that Philip was hearing the voices quite often, for we could sometimes hear him answering quietly. The sadness would return to his face and was deeply distressing to watch. Such was our concern that we again spoke to the consultants at the hospital about it, and they promised to review Philip's medication to see if it could be improved. Meanwhile, all we could do was to try to help Philip when he seemed to need our help the most, but it was a far from easy task.

It was about this time too, that Philip again began to come

home early from the hospital. The same situation as before seemed to be repeating itself. It was so wearisome, having to repeat again and again to Philip that he *must* go along to the hospital. He would apologise, and promise that it wouldn't happen again. However tiring it seemed to us, we knew we had to persevere. We couldn't give up what seemed to be our never-ending battle of endurance.

Yes! there were certainly times when I got angry with Philip, especially when what I said to him didn't seem to 'get through', making it necessary for me to repeat myself again and again. And there were times when I often reached the end of my tether. How much longer could it go on? I would ask myself repeatedly. But then Philip would have a 'good' spell when he was loving, and this seemed to cancel out the 'bad' days—or at least make me more able to tolerate them.

As I write these words, I am moved that my most vivid, lasting memory of Philip is of those good days when he was happy and giving, showing and sharing his love so freely— so much a part of his normal personality. It was almost as though he was making up for lost time in his efforts to reach us.

One Wednesday, late in January, our lives changed completely, and our world came tumbling around us in chaos. It had started out much the same as any other day, with Iain and Carol going off to school as usual. As on so many previous occasions, Philip had to be coerced into going along to the day hospital. I must confess there had been times when I was tempted to give in, such was the pressure upon me; but then I would realise that it was for Philip's long-term good that he must attend, and so I must persevere.

I recall that on the Tuesday evening, when we were all having tea together, Philip had been unusually quiet until he suddenly began to mutter under his breath. For the first time we could actually hear him swearing back at the voices! His face was contorted with pain and distress, obviously caused by what he was hearing. Almost immediately, however, he 'came back to us'.

'Sorry mum, sorry dad,' he said.

Perhaps I am wrong, but I feel that Philip thought we could actually hear what the voices were saying to him. We told him that it was all right, that he mustn't worry, and we tried to put the incident out of our minds.

Iain and Carol were obviously aware of their brother's distress, for they too showed concern. True, they had found life difficult during the time leading up to Philip's illness. It had been hard for them to understand his behaviour and actions, particularly when he was at his most belligerent towards them. Now, however, they were realising just what Philip was going through, and they showed a deep concern for him. It was touching to see this concern in them, to know that in spite of all they had been through, and despite the fact that they were only young teenagers themselves— they now felt for their brother's plight. All of us were in this together, and we all felt the hurt of it, though Philip suffered most of all. We were reminded that his illness was a constant struggle for Philip. All any of us could do was look on helplessly. We were so devastated that we couldn't even pray.

Philip returned home from hospital on that particular Wednesday—the next day—even earlier than usual. I remember that it was a bitterly cold day as I opened the door to him. He stood on the doorstep, his face very red from exposure to the cold air and from running home after getting off the bus. His face was beaming, though, and he looked the picture of physical health and vitality.

I gave him another telling off, pointing out to him that he was leaving the hospital earlier than ever. He would stay longer in future, he promised, and although we 'had words' about it, the incident passed quickly, and the rest of that afternoon was spent as any other. Philip listened to his records in his room for a while, and then watched a video on television as he often did. Then we had a talk for a time about ordinary, everyday things, and for most of the time he was in good spirits. True, he did have moments when he relapsed into his trance-like state, quiet and withdrawn into himself, but there was nothing unusual about that. It was the way he had often behaved since the onset of his illness.

By now tea-time was approaching. Dusk was falling early. Suddenly, Philip came into the kitchen wearing his jacket.

'I'm just going out for a walk,' he said. (This wasn't unusual, he often popped out for a half hour's walk.)

'OK, but don't be long, tea will soon be ready,' I replied.

'OK,' he said, and off he went.

I had just heard the last words my son would ever speak to me; surely Philip did not realise they would be the last words he would ever utter? Absolutely nothing had suggested to me the horror of what was to happen—nothing out of the ordinary to give me any indication whatsoever.

An hour passed by, but there was no sign of Philip. I wasn't unduly anxious at first, because Philip had often stayed out as long before, particularly if he had called to see one of his friends. Hence I assumed he had done so again on this occasion.

Still more time went by, and *still* no sign of Philip. I began to get worried! I remember I went to the front gate to see if he was coming down the road. No sign of him.

It was bitterly cold, with a hard frost, and by now it was completely dark. It was not the sort of evening for anyone to be out. I hurried back into the house and looked at the clock yet again. My worry was mounting, and I looked out of the window to see if Philip was returning. Suddenly, a police car drew up outside the house, and out stepped a policeman. I couldn't believe that he would walk up to our front door— but alas, he did. My heart sank; I immediately sensed that something had happened.

There came the inevitable knock on the front door, which

I nervously opened. He was quite brief, the young officer who stood before me. He said Philip had fallen over some railings, and it was thought had broken his legs. He didn't have any more information yet, adding only that Philip was in the casualty department of the local hospital. He offered to take me there, and off we went. John was working in Macclesfield with the Hallé that evening, so we had to go without him.

All I can recall thinking on that short journey to the hospital was that for Philip to have broken his legs was bad enough, but thank goodness it was no worse! Already I was convincing myself he would be all right.

It was only when we reached the hospital, however, that the full enormity of it all hit me. A rather harsh, unsympathetic police officer told me that Philip had walked along the parapet of a bridge and fallen on to the hard-shoulder of the motorway below.

It was all too much to grasp. I was utterly confused. What did it all mean? Why was Philip on the bridge in the first place?

Suddenly the policeman asked in a rather curt, straightforward manner, 'Has he done anything like this before?'

'No,' I replied. Although I had answered him honestly, the full implication of his question hadn't reached me. I was still too bewildered. Even when he asked me if Philip was depressed at all, the significance of what he was saying still didn't strike me. 'No,' I answered again, 'but Philip is suffering from schizophrenia, not depression.' The officer seemed to discount my reply, almost as though he was indifferent to the idea of schizophrenia.

During the next hour, first one doctor would come to talk to me and ask me questions, then another. The sister on duty came too! Little by little they told me the full extent of Philip's injuries as they saw them on the X-ray plates. The broken legs, they discovered, were not his only injuries by any means.

By this time I felt completely dazed. Suddenly I realised something very important: I wanted to see Philip. 'Yes,' they said when I asked, I would be able to see him in a few minutes.

Not until I actually saw Philip for myself did I fully feel the impact of what had happened. Even then I was under the impression that he had been sedated. When I asked, however, they told me he hadn't. Philip was losing consciousness, and his injuries were bad. It was all so difficult to believe.

A nurse there was most concerned because I was alone. I should have someone with me—she insisted—a relative or friend. Since our relatives do not live in Manchester, I thought about which of our friends could be contacted. Two were sent for, and both—Eileen and Margaret—came promptly. How relieved I felt when they arrived, for I badly needed their support. The Salvation Army officer of the local corps, Captain Robin McIntosh, came too. I don't know what I would have done without them.

Later on, having at last been reached, John arrived by taxi. The police had managed to locate the hall where the Hallé was giving its concert that night. John looked shocked and stunned by it all; he too found it hard to believe what had happened. Then, some time after John had arrived, the medical staff decided that Philip should be transferred to Manchester Royal Infirmary, where he was to undergo major surgery. The transfer quickly took place.

And so began the longest night of our lives, as we began our vigil for our son. Three of us sat through that night: John, Captain Robin McIntosh, and I. We were so thankful that this gentle man of God was able to be with us that night. His presence was a great support, one we greatly needed. He was sensitive to our needs, silent when he thought it best; but he spoke with us when the moment was appropriate, for which we were thankful.

The night crept slowly on, each hour seeming to pass

more slowly than the previous one, as we waited for news of our son. Although we felt utterly exhausted, we remained wide awake the whole time. When at last the operation was over, Philip was taken to intensive care. After quite some time, two of the doctors came to talk to us. They kept nothing back, although they were very kind. It was, in their opinion, they said, very unlikely that Philip would pull through, due to the extent of his injuries. Usually, in their experience, people with such injuries did not survive. Although I heard and understood all they were saying, their words just did not convince me, for I really believed that Philip would live. He hadn't come through all the heartache and suffering of his illness and this terrible accident—to die! Surely, God in his love would let Philip live.

I was searching my mind. People who had been involved in serious accidents had pulled through against the odds! I was trying to convince myself, willing Philip to live.

After what seemed like hours and hours, we were taken to a waiting room in the intensive care unit and told we would be able to see Philip in a while. I remember that as we sat in that room, silently waiting to be called in to see Philip, we talked together from time to time. Much of what we said is now rather vague with all the confusion, and in fact for most of the time we were silent. I distinctly remember though, looking out of the window. In the distance I could see the snow gently falling by the dim light of a street lamp. Even in that moment, amidst all the turmoil of the past hours and the nightmarish uncertainty of whether Philip was going to live or die, there somehow came to me a calmness, an inner assurance that everything would be all right.

Suddenly, the doctors came again into the room. We could see Philip now, they said, but they still made it clear that Philip's condition was very serious. Then they led us quietly through the unit to Philip's bedside.

We sat there for a while. I cannot describe my feelings as I looked at him. I found it too difficult to remain there for long, and suddenly felt that I had to leave the hospital and return home to Carol and Iain. John, however, stayed at Philip's bedside. I felt that getting away from the hospital for just a little while would help me, that I would then be able to return to Philip again—so I came home.

I had been at home for only half an hour when the 'phone rang. I didn't want to answer it—not then—for somehow I knew instinctively where the call was from. But the 'phone was as remorseless as the knock on the door. It had to be answered, whether I wanted to or not.

John's voice at the other end of the line was choked. 'It's all over—Philip has gone.' That was all he was able to say.

I returned to the hospital almost immediately but not before first breaking the news to Iain and Carol. The look of disbelief on their faces said it all! But although they were deeply upset, they remained calm. Friends stayed with them that morning while John and I were at the hospital.

When I returned, the hospital sister suggested that I may want to see Philip again. Yes!—that was what I wanted. John stayed in the sister's office.

I stood over Philip, and still found it difficult to believe that he had gone. I cradled his face between my hands. This was the darkest moment of my life. I felt the ultimate in human pain as the crushing realisation dawned on me that Philip had died. That his life was no more. Yes, it was true—it *had* happened.

As I looked on his broken body, it all seemed so cruel, so hard. What was the point of it all—that he should have to die after all he had been through? A young boy whose whole life had lain before him, a life of such promise, such potential. While he had lived, while he had struggled against the illness which had devastated his mind, his very being, there was always a source of hope: hope that by some miracle he might one day be well again; a whole person, free to enjoy life to the full. Goodness knows, he had fought so hard to be free, and fought to the last.

Now he was gone! I felt deeply lost and hurt. I remember saying to the nurse who was standing close by: 'He's only sixteen, that's all, sixteen.'

'I know, dear,' she said, quite overcome herself.

As I lingered there in those moments, the thought did cross my mind 'What a waste!' (It's very strange, but I was to actually hear those same words repeated several times during the next few days.) Was it a waste? I was too shocked and confused to have an answer at that moment. Yet for all my feelings of disbelief and utter despair about Philip's death, amidst the hurt and anger I felt (and the confusion too), there did come to me a strange sense of calm and peace.

The nurse gently led me away from Philip's bedside. I knew, as I left my son for the last time, that much as I had loved him during his life, the fact of his death didn't alter that love, for there would always be a deep love for him within me.

John and I left the hospital much later that morning, after official requirements had been carried out for the police enquiries and the future inquest. What we most needed then was to return home to Iain and Carol. They very much needed us. We needed them. We all needed each other.

Two or three days later, I remember sitting in our living room early one morning. I had found sleep difficult, and had awoken early. Suddenly I heard the clatter of the letter-box as the post arrived. During those first days, we received many cards and letters of condolence from kind friends and relatives; from acquaintances, too, and our kind neighbours. We were cushioned and borne along by the love and support of others, which helped us enormously, and for which we were grateful.

Of all the many cards which we received, one tiny card in particular stood out from the rest. Its words, based on a verse of the psalms, simply read:

> Sorrow is but the guest of a night.
> Joy cometh in the morning.

At that precise moment, I couldn't take in the full meaning of those words, for I was still utterly numb and shocked at losing Philip. Yet, somehow, those words penetrated my numbness and touched me deeply. 'Joy cometh in the morning!' And as I pondered on those words, a great sense of peace and calm again returned to me, even at such a dark time.

When I later told John how I felt, he said he too had experienced an inner peace and calm. Having talked over our feelings with each other, we came to the conclusion that the trauma of those past months was likened to a raging thunderstorm, when it seems that the earth shakes beneath one's feet with the fury of the elements. Fear of such a storm can make one tremble and become deeply disturbed, and the question of survival is uppermost. But then comes the calm.

We had felt like that! We had questioned whether we could come through all the worry, anxiety and heartache. We had asked ourselves many times when and how it would all come to an end. And yet, in spite of our great sorrow and grief at losing our son, we had both felt this sense of inner peace and calm! At the time, this strange experience seemed almost too difficult to understand, even a little disturbing— as though we should have felt differently.

It almost seemed as though Philip's new-found peace was our peace too—the difference being that our lives would continue exactly as before, here on Earth, while Philip's life had just begun in Eternity.

9

From Sorrow to Joy

The first days after Philip's death passed, and so arrived the day of his funeral.

Funerals—none of us cares to think about them; we wish the day over and done with as quickly as possible, presumably because of the inner fear of death most of us feel. However strong our faith in life after death may be, we are never quite so painfully aware that we are saying goodbye for the last time on earth to our loved ones as on the day of their funeral.

We felt somewhat like that as the time approached for Philip's service, for no matter how painful, we knew we had to face it. And I make no apologies for pausing to reflect a little on Philip's service, because however else it could be described, it certainly wasn't morbid!

We had thought carefully about the service beforehand, with as much concentration as we were able to muster. We wanted a tribute made to Philip during the service.

We didn't have to give this matter much thought before 'Uncle Norman' came to our minds. He had meant so much to Philip during his life, but we realised that it wasn't an easy task for Norman to undertake. As he spoke, a hushed silence fell over the congregation. He spoke of the days when Philip, as a young boy, had been full of vitality; of how he had joined in with the other boys in fun; and yet, in spite of his mischievous nature, Philip had come to realise and accept the real meaning of attending Sunday School—Philip knew that Jesus was a friend and Saviour to whoever believed in him.

I will always remember Norman's final words as he concluded his tribute. He simply said: 'Goodbye, Philip. See you—in the morning.'

Those poignant words again struck at my own heart very forcibly, for they were the same words I had read on the tiny card received a few days previously—the same reference to 'the eternal morning'.

We had been deeply touched by the large number of people attending Philip's service, for among them were several of Philip's former teachers—his headmaster, who had tried so hard to help those months earlier, two nurses from the day hospital, and a social worker. Together with our relatives, friends, business colleagues and acquaintances, these all attended to pay their respects to Philip.

Superficially viewed, the tragedy of Philip's death—the funeral being over, the last of our relatives and friends having returned home after offering us their support, as well as paying their last respects to Philip—might seem to be the final chapter in the story of Philip's life. In the event, however, this was far from the case, for although Philip's life had come to an end, his memory remained.

The feeling of numbed shock, of being somehow anaesthetised, seemed to linger for several weeks. It was a strange, weird sensation, almost like being engulfed in a mist of 'nothingness'. I felt strangely disturbed by my own feelings—or lack of them!—for during those first weeks I had very little desire to weep; and even when I did, my tears seemed somehow superficial, not from within. It was difficult to understand, this lack of 'real' feeling, for I expected to be more upset than I actually was. I did not realise at the time, that this is a normal reaction. My tired mind had taken such a pounding during the many months of Philip's illness, followed by the tragic circumstances of his death, that it was little wonder that my mind had 'shut off'—switched over, somehow, to automatic. Life's everyday events carried on almost as though nothing had happened. There is, after all, a limit to what each one of us can take, no matter how strong we each consider ourselves to be.

The first year following Philip's death was by far the worst of all! Each event was a first time without him. May, his birthday month, was particularly painful, as were Christmas, Easter, and the summer holiday period. Indeed, as each anniversary we had all previously shared as a family came around, we were made all the more painfully aware of Philip's absence. Oh, how I missed him! Missed his very being, his presence in and around our home. His absence emphasised the terrible void he had left behind—and yet, he *had* gone! We had to face that, even though facing it brought a seemingly endless hurt.

During those dreadful early days, my mind, unbidden, also continually recalled the time when Philip's illness had been at its most devastating. I clearly remembered the occasion when he had had to be hospitalised against his will, and I could still see him, in my mind's eye, sitting dejected and lonely on his bed, feeling utterly rejected, as if unloved by anyone. I recalled this scene vividly and frequently; and on each occasion the memory upset me deeply. At such times the question would come again: *Why? Why did Philip have to suffer such a cruel illness?*

And if schizophrenia *had* to be his lot, why could he not have been among the lucky ones, one of the small minority who make a recovery? When his illness had first been diagnosed, we had desperately clung to the hope of a cure for him, given time. Then these hopes were finally crushed, dashed to pieces when Philip's life came so unexpectedly to an end on that chilling January day. At that point it seemed that there was no further hope left to cling to for comfort. So often, in those dark days, we heard the familiar cliche, 'Time is a great healer!' We *wanted* to believe it, but it was so difficult to accept while struggling with such intense grief. I was well aware of the fragile state of my emotions, of my extreme vulnerability, yet I felt totally unable to do anything about it to help myself. All I *could* do was wait! It wasn't a case of 'giving in'—more of 'holding on'.

Quite by chance one day, I came across these words from the Psalms of David:

> Be merciful unto me, O God, be merciful unto me; for my soul trusteth in Thee. Yea, in the shadow of Thy wings will I make my refuge, until these calamities be overpast (Psalm 57:1).

If ever I needed a refuge, a protection—if ever I needed to trust in God's promise that he would sustain us until this darkness had passed from our life—it was then. I knew that herein lay our answer. I must place all our grief, questionings, doubts, and agonies in God's hands, and wait in faith for his healing to come.

And come it did, but it was not an immediate, miraculous thing. The grief didn't suddenly disappear. Yet, as the weeks passed by, light began gently to filter through the darkness which at times had almost overwhelmed us. The space between the bad days began to widen, and good days replaced them; and I was able for the first time since the tragedy to look at the whole situation far more objectively.

It had caused pain, confusion—and yes, even anger—that God had not answered our prayers for Philip's healing in the way we had asked. But as time passed and our grief began slowly to diminish, then, just as surely, came the realisation that the hope we had had for Philip's healing was not to be realised in this life. Yet our own healing was, by God's grace, taking place, and we now had not only the hope, but the comfort and assurance of *knowing* that Philip's healing and wholeness was complete, now that he was safe in God's heavenly keeping.

No more would he have to fight, as in this life, to be free of the struggle and torment which had imprisoned him. He was free. He had arrived—HOME! What more could be wished or hoped for our son?

What then is this book about? Is it about illness, suffering (both of mind and body), death, heartache, sadness, agony and near-despair? Ah, yes, it *is* about all of those things. But more, much more! For it is also about happiness—love, peace, understanding, joy—and above all else *hope*: that life, even when it looks full of defeat and despair, can be turned to hope; that even in the depth of sadness and sorrow we must know that this need not be the end; that the sun still shines behind the black cloud in the darkened sky.

As I reflect again on Philip's life, I ponder on all he has left behind. No, not some great achievement, but in his short time here on earth he left something far, far more precious. He left behind *love*, which touched not only us, his family, but which reached out to others also.

We had no idea all those years ago, when Philip was first given into our care by God for us to nurture and love, just what an influence he was to have upon our lives. And now, as I look back upon Philip's passing, I see not only what we have lost, but also what we have gained through him. Certainly, Philip's life and death touched many people's hearts. Many, I believe, were made aware for the first time of life's deeper levels. Many lives were touched—but none more so than that of my own! I am a richer person; my existence has taken on more meaning—all because God touched my life through one special person—our dear son, Philip.

I thank God that he gave Philip to us, even though it could only be for such a short time, until he released Philip from all the heartache, pain and suffering of this life. I am assured and calm within myself now, knowing for certain that Philip is safe with God in heaven.

He is at peace. I am at peace.

There will always be a special place in our hearts for the

memory of Philip, and for the time being I can say: 'Good-bye my son, my beloved son! See you "in the morning".'

> Let the words of my mouth, and the meditation of my heart, be acceptable in thy sight, O Lord, my strength, and my redeemer (Psalm 19:14).

Part II

Hope For Those
Who Care

There is a tide in the affairs of men
Which taken at the flood leads on to fortune. . . .
On such a full sea are we now afloat,
And we must take the current when it serves
Or lose our ventures.

Shakespeare, *Julius Caesar* IV, iii

Christian faith and psychiatry have viewed each other with suspicion for too long, especially as both have in common the wish to alleviate suffering and lead men and women to health and wholeness.

Conflict must give way to co-operation for the sake of the victims of such destructive mental diseases as schizophrenia. The unique contribution of the Christian faith to the illness is its ability to see, over and above human limitations and disturbances, the image of God; and to apply the indefinable yet unique contribution of Christian love to make community care a reality in our society.

The Christian faith can embrace new psychological insights without betraying its heritage or diluting its message; while psychiatry can only be strengthened by acknowledging the unique contribution of the Christian faith to the healing and salvation of all.

Dr Nigel Cameron, in his introduction to the series, writes that Christians 'have no option but to care for others', thus emphasising that caring is part of Christian tradition. One of the approaches we may adopt, says Dr Cameron, is by practical caring for those round about us. This book gives an excellent example of the kind of people who need such care.

David Enoch

1

Schizophrenia: The Onset

Ignorance and fear are two powerful forces that have prevented the advancement of care both for the victims of schizophrenia and for their carers. Opposing extreme attitudes have, however, conspired latterly to create a new awareness of the problems. On the one hand, a group of ex-patients, together with some professionals, even oppose recognition of the existence of the illness of schizophrenia and its allied states. They also oppose specific treatments such as drug therapy and admission into hospital. Such attitudes towards the illness arose as a result of the writings of Laing and Szasz in the 1960s, when it was suggested that mental illness was a myth and that schizophrenia could be talked away. These attitudes have now been discredited, although they still hover around.

Ranged on the other side are those who have tried to cope with the illness, such as the carers and relatives. They complain bitterly that, as the trend is towards moving treatment from the hospital to the community, there has been an associated neglect of schizophrenics and also a lack of concern and support for the carers, even during acute crises.

There is thus an increasing concern in the media, including television and the newspapers, for this group of suffering people. Hence Mary Moate's beautiful yet tragic story of her schizophrenic son comes at a most opportune time. She is an advocate—an eloquent one—for those who have and do suffer from schizophrenia, as well as for the carers such as the relatives. Pointing out in particular the great suffering of Philip, her son, and the associated suffering of herself, her husband and Philip's two siblings, her account gives us an opportunity to redress the balance; to describe the scientific facts about this illness, admit the limitations, and suggest a balanced way forward to manage and treat schizophrenics and their carers.

We are at present 'on such a full sea...' and we certainly must 'take the current when it serves' (to use the words of Shakespeare's Brutus), to try to reduce—if not completely eliminate—the ignorance and the fear which surrounds this tragic illness. Above all what is necessary is a balanced view of the illness, a clear understanding of the mode of presentation of the symptoms involved and of the appropriate way to treat and manage the illness, as well to acknowledge the support needed by the carers.

The myths surrounding schizophrenia are many and complicated. Often mental illness is equated with schizophrenia; thus it must be emphasised that whereas schizophrenia is a severe form of mental illness, not all mental illnesses are made up of schizophrenia. Again, the illness, though severe, is not contagious; although often the reaction of family and friends (and even Christians) towards the victims and their families suggests that they consider it to be so. One mother once told me that this is what she found hard to accept, for when her son developed the illness, not only did he lose his numerous friends, but also friends of the family began to desert them one by one. This desertion was linked with a definite feeling that in some way their children would be caught up in the illness and be contaminated by it. It is such ignorance and fear that causes additional, and indeed, unnecessary distress to both victim and family.

As implied, some of the present attitudes to schizophrenia

have also arisen because of the shift of emphasis from the hospital to the community and the need for community care. As a result of this change in some parts of the country, relatives and carers have found that schizophrenics have had difficulties being readmitted into hospital when symptoms recur or worsen. Numerous parents have felt frightened of pushing for the return of their sons and daughters to hospital, lest this be interpreted as their wanting to be rid of them. They feel heavily the continual burden upon them, one that they will face for years to come, with no chance of relief. It has been suggested that whereas previously the policy was 'lock away', now it is a question of 'lock out'; both policies have grievous consequences to both patients and carers.

The conspiracy of silence

In spite of one extreme opinion which denies its existence, it is an established fact that a set of symptoms known as 'schizophrenia' does exist. Indeed one of the first major points of Mary Moate's account is the fact that she felt Philip *did* suffer from schizophrenia long before anybody else was prepared to make a firm diagnosis. It is striking that, although she faced the possibility and indeed believed that Philip was suffering from schizophrenia and learned that this was so, she still demanded a firm diagnosis.

Often as a doctor I have been faced with relatives bringing their adolescents and young men and women to me fearful that the illness might well turn out to be schizophrenia, but at the same time demanding a firm diagnosis. Sometimes it may well be difficult to make such a firm diagnosis, especially during the early phase of the illness, but some time or another it is essential that a firm diagnosis, if at all possible, is made. Diagnosis is merely the first step towards appropriate treatment and management. In spite of their fear of the diagnosis and their anxiety regarding the future, relatives have thanked me when I have eventually said to them as gently as possible, yet firmly, that I believed that their son or daughter was suffering from schizophrenia.

In spite of being fearful early on that her son might be suffering from the dreaded illness of schizophrenia, then, Mary Moate sought a firm diagnosis. And only when she did receive it did she believe that both her son and carers would be able to face the situation in an effective way. There is nothing to gain by a conspiracy of silence. Nor should the doctors, if they do have a firm diagnosis, pretend to being unable to share with the relatives the true situation.

Strikingly, schizophrenia occurs in all the civilised countries of the world and in the same proportion of one to one hundred. In the United Kingdom alone, therefore, there are 300,000 people who have had a diagnosis of schizophrenia at some time. Thus at any given time there are 150,000 sufferers. The annual cost to the NHS has been estimated as about £200 million, of which surprisingly only 4% is used for anti-psychotic medication. The diagnosis is sometimes over-used especially in some parts of the world such as the USA; however, there is also a danger of the condition being missed if great precision in clinical assessment is not forthcoming.

A prompt, accurate diagnosis

As a consultant physician in psychological medicine dealing with such cases, I have been in practice long enough to remember when there were no specific effective drugs which could be used to remove the most severe and positive symptoms of the illness such as delusions and hallucinations. I then witnessed the revolution in treatment which began in the mid 1950s. Through this and through optimistic attitudes towards the mentally ill which already existed among professional staff, we saw a miraculous change occur in the patients within mental hospitals.

Only subsequently, as a result of their own improvement, did patients themselves begin to enquire why they had to remain in hospital. Here it must be emphasised that the move from the hospital to the community began not with politicians, administrators or even doctors, but with *patients*. It thus became clear not only that schizophrenia was a real problem but that with early diagnosis, appropriate treatment and management, patients *could* remain and be treated in the community. Even those who were admitted did not need to remain forever in such institutions, but would again, with appropriate treatment, improve sufficiently to return to the community.

Such a trend in treatment is not invalidated because there might well have been some mismanagement of patients who have been transferred into the community or who develop schizophrenia for the first time. For difficulties can occur, and carers are put under great pressure as a result of the reluctance of some psychiatrists and general practitioners, social workers and nurses to accept that deterioration has occurred—to such an extent that readmission is necessary. This thought has been reinforced by the numerous letters and phone calls I have received following the publication of my book, *Healing the Hurt Mind*, from desperate parents seeking advice and active support for sons and daughters who are deteriorating, but do not seem to have the necessary correct management. These carers describe clearly, as does Mrs Moate, the great disruption that can occur in the family as a result of the mental deterioration of the patient.

Timing is therefore of the essence—timing in the making of an appropriate firm diagnosis, timing in informing the relatives, and timing in the admission or readmission into hospital if that becomes necessary.

Schizophrenia—the 'splintered mind'

In schizophrenia, no physical lesion can be seen by the naked eye (there is therefore no macroscopic lesion or damage in the brain). Hence schizophrenia has been called a 'functional psychosis' or 'insanity'. There is, however, a widespread belief that schizophrenia is a medical condition and has a physical basis in that the schizophrenic may well be found to have an inherent dysfunction of the chemistry of the brain.

Although we do not yet know schizophrenia's exact cause, it is regarded as a severe form of mental illness because of the severity of the symptoms. These cause the person to lose insight and become divorced from reality; the destruction of the normal personality often leads to a deterioration in behaviour and accomplishments, much to the distress of the family and carers. It is a fallacy, however, to believe that schizophrenia is a condition of a split mind like that of Dr Jekyll and Mr Hyde, for the splitting occurs between thought and feeling. It would be more appropriate, perhaps, to describe schizophrenia as 'a splintered mind', in that the mind is fragmented by the progress of the disease, during the course of which (as Mrs Moate so clearly describes in the case of her son) the normal capacities for behaviour—perceiving, thinking, feeling and even physical movements—disintegrate to various degrees.

Another fallacy is that the term 'schizophrenia' is always applicable for a specific clear-cut illness. Unfortunately, it is often used as an all-embracing term to cover a number of different kinds of illnesses, though it must be emphasised that the true primary schizophrenic illness can be quite well described in clinical terms.

Acute schizophrenic symptoms may occur suddenly, severely, yet clear up equally quickly and completely. It may, however, be associated with certain stresses such as childbirth, or it may occur quite spontaneously. Again, schizophrenic symptoms may occur in the setting of a severe mood change such as depression or mania. In this case the disease is referred to as *schizo-affective psychosis*. Other schizophrenic-like symptoms may occur in acute or severe form quite spontaneously or as a result of some stimulus and may then clear completely. Or perhaps they may be followed by a further episode, which again is short-lived and transient. Such episodes are termed *schizophreniform psychosis*.

In considering the symptoms of schizophrenia it is important to know that stimulant and hallucinogenic groups of drugs can produce a clinical state resembling schizophrenia. Amphetamine psychosis can be caused by large doses of amphetamines as well as occasionally by low doses taken as appetite suppressants. The outstanding feature is usually a paranoid state, ie, ideas of persecution—although excitement resembling mania can also occur. Sometimes, even after the drug has been stopped and the urine is clear of it, some of these features persist.

Hallucinogenic drugs such as LSD can also precipitate a schizophrenic episode. In most cases these schizophrenic symptoms clear a few weeks or months after the drug is discontinued; however, in a relatively small percentage of cases, the schizophrenic process persists and may even worsen. In the latter group, it may well be that the LSD precipitated or awakened a latent schizophrenia. In the same way cannabis can produce various kinds of mental disorders including schizophrenic-like pictures. Usually these clear up after the cannabis is stopped, but a few cases continue, suggesting that there was a pre-existing psychiatric disorder.

The first days

We are still left with schizophrenia, a primary illness which Mrs Moate describes and accepts as the diagnosis in Philip's case. She describes clearly the anxiety that she initially experienced when she realised the possibility of this diagnosis. She had a premonition that this 'dreadful illness' was the cause of her son's changed behaviour. And although she obviously hoped against hope that it would not be so, she nevertheless wanted the doctors to make a correct and firm diagnosis; rightly surmising that only then would Philip receive prompt and proper attention and management. This is one of the outstanding contributions of her account: her willingness to share with us the feelings of the close relatives and carers of the schizophrenic; the initial vague anxiety, then the dawning of the fact that the illness might indeed turn out to be the dreaded schizophrenia.

Doctors and other professionals must learn to be sensitive to this very specific anxiety at this particular time and to be able to be interpreters of the symptoms and the condition. Graciously, sensitively, yet firmly, they should be able to communicate with the patient and also—equally important—with the immediate relatives, what is the true state of affairs and the diagnosis. Perhaps because of justifiable professional detachment, or perhaps because of an *un*justifiable lack of knowledge of the true suffering of the patients and their relatives, we may not have succeeded as well as we could in the past at this particular phase of the illness. With the increased understanding which should result from greater knowledge of the illness, and with the clear advocacy of Mrs Moate, it is imperative to emphasise now the need for this sensitivity at the very first phase of the illness. If Mrs Moate's story succeeds only in encouraging this sensitivity, it will have been of great value.

Mrs Moate reminds us that there is no need for an apology for following the medical model—firstly making a diagnosis and then formulating a plan of management and treatment. This is the way of clinical medicine, and as psychiatrists we are first and foremost physicians. Perhaps we have been influenced too much by other forces, with such an exaggerated emphasis on the multi-disciplinary approach that we have been less prepared to carry out the usual clinical examination leading to as firm a diagnosis as possible, as early as possible. But in deviating from precise clinical assessment and diagnosis, we not only do a great disservice to ourselves but may well cause unintentional but unnecessary harm to the patient and delay his recovery. This sensitive account of the suffering of Philip and his carers reinforces, therefore, the need for a correct and early diagnosis based upon the medical model and a clear-cut plan of management and treatment for the patient and support for carers from the very beginning.

This need for adequate assessment and proper treatment is also revealed in the heartfelt cry of David Reed for his 'Anna'. 'Anna', a beautiful young mother of two small children, with a history of recurring schizophrenic break-downs, was encouraged by 'a Laingian doctor' to face her own madness without recourse to physical treatment. How-ever, realising the inadequacy of this form of treatment, her husband cried out in a letter to Laing: '... the weeks of psychosis were unnecessary and could have been halted at the beginning.... I relate this not to hurt you, Roy, but because it hurts *me* so much.' [1] This husband as well as others have cried out in anguish that a few injections of Largactil or Modecate rather than months of talking would have saved their loved ones tremendous suffering. Of course the patient himself is unlikely to appreciate this; lack of insight is characteristic of the schizophrenic. This fact only makes responsibility of the carer even more pertinent than in many other medical and psychological illnesses.

Often, general practitioners find it difficult to make a firm diagnosis when presented with disturbed behaviour in young adolescents. The behaviour can be readily explained as their natural passage through adolescence, with all its inherent difficulties. Also, the general practitioner is not geared towards making the awful diagnosis of schizophrenia and anyway is usually inexperienced in dealing with such cases. Meanwhile a parent who, like Mrs Moate, intuitively knows that a child is gravely ill mentally, is reluctant to put forward her thoughts because she might give the impression that she wanted her child to be sent away. And again, unfortunately, such mothers fear the professional stance,

---

[1] David Reed, *Anna* (Penguin: 1977), p 172.

believing that their suggestions might be thwarted merely because a layman has made them. As a doctor I am reluctant to accept that these are barriers to diagnosis, but the evidence of many parents has to outweigh my reluctance!

In order then to reach the correct diagnosis of schizophrenia, the doctor must adhere to certain clinical procedures. A detailed history must be taken from the patient and from an informed relative, followed by a full physical and mental state examination. The patient might well have to be seen and examined on more than one occasion, and the doctor would have to interview other independent witnesses of the disturbed behaviour and change in personality. During the examination symptoms will be noted, some of which will be strongly suggestive of schizophrenia and others merely suggestive, as well as negative symptoms which, though not essential for the diagnosis of schizophrenia, are important in assessing prognosis and choosing the form of management. These negative symptoms can also cause increasing acrimony within families, as well as a great deal of frustration, irritability and even anger. To these and other symptoms we turn in the next chapter.

2

Signs and Symptoms of Schizophrenia

Schizophrenia most characteristically reveals itself, as in Philip's case, during the years of young adulthood or adolescence. In a substantial number the onset is so insidious as to make it almost impossible to detect exactly when the illness actually commenced. Mrs Moate's account shows clearly how normal Philip's behaviour was as a baby and child. While she herself wondered later whether she and her husband had missed any early clues to the advent of this illness, it is clear from her account that his babyhood and childhood were normal. Indeed, they enjoyed life as a family to the full, even more so after the introduction of the twins. Philip's boisterousness was well within normal limits; his concern for his mother's love after the twins had joined the family was equally so. His apparent slowness at school would not be a sign of schizophrenia, though it would become a factor for consideration when the prognosis of the illness would be considered later.

Major manifestations

The most common characteristic disturbances found in schizophrenia include all those listed in the headings following.

Primary delusions

Delusions are false and often irrational beliefs which are held with unshakable conviction and which cannot be dispelled by any logical argument or apt persuasion. A sudden delusion arising out of the blue—one that is not related to any prior perception, image or memory—is a very strong indication of the presence of schizophrenia. One common delusion is when the person believes that one or more people are deliberately persecuting him and wanting to harm him. He may believe that he is being poisoned. Other patients may suffer from other kinds of delusions—such as delusions of grandeur—being convinced that they are Napoleon, a king, or some other well-known person from history or still living. Another significant delusion is the schizophrenic's belief that his mind or body is under the control of another person or agency. This belief is known as 'feelings of passivity'.

Another important form of delusion is that of *delusional perception*, when the person has a sudden conviction that an experience has a special meaning. He will believe that people talk about him disparagingly. Sometimes this delusion will occur as a religious or grandiose idea. The *sudden* transition from commonplace to delusional thinking is the important and indicative feature which makes one suspicious. Accompanying it is the change of behaviour Mrs Moate noticed in Philip.

A *delusional mood* is what the patient 'feels' when things in his environment take on a special significance for him. This 'feeling' intensifies and causes him to be confused and perplexed. Often the schizophrenic in the initial phase of the illness will describe himself as being 'confused' and 'perplexed' because he does not know what is happening to him. While this is not a sufficient basis of diagnosis, not infrequently this delusional mood gives way eventually to obvious primary delusions.

Hallucinations

Hallucinations are the perception of hearing, seeing, smelling or feeling things which do not exist in reality. When they do occur they are very striking and can be bewildering, especially to the onlooker. They are symptoms, together with the delusion(s), which cause grave concern in the layman onlooker and the relative, friend or carer. This is especially true if they occur in a previously healthy, normal person.

When they do occur, the most common form of hallucinations in schizophrenia are the auditory type. The patient states that he hears a 'voice or voices', which no one else can hear, talking about him and referring to him in the third person. Often the patient reveals that the 'voices' refer to him disparagingly (demonstrating a paranoid element), and may comment on his actions and suggest what he should do. The voice(s) may appear to come from within the patient's head, within his body or from outside.

Hallucinations are strongly suggestive of schizophrenia, in the absence of other mental illness such as mood disorders, depressive illness or mania. In the former the patient would be severely depressed, in the latter, on a 'high'—abnormally euphoric and happy.

Disorders of thought

The schizophrenic quite typically has difficulty in thinking clearly, logically and cohesively. He will also find it difficult or impossible to concentrate. He may find it difficult to link one thought directly with another; he may interchange cause and effect, draw illogical conclusions, and talk a stream of nonsense known only to himself—invented to explain his illogical ideas and thoughts to himself and others.

Other kinds of thought disorder occur. He may complain that thoughts are being 'withdrawn' or 'inserted' into his brain by some external agency which he cannot control, and of which no one else can have knowledge or access.

He may show 'thought blocking': rapidly changing in his

speech from one topic to another unrelated one. This indicates that the schizophrenic experiences passively the sudden stopping of his brain or thought. There is nothing in the schizophrenic's mind at this time, and no amount of prompting will get him to express his thoughts. (Here I am making a contrast with losing one's thread of thought because of intense anxiety; in such moments a person is merely trying to find the right word to say, but his thought processes do go on.)

Thought broadcasting occurs where the subject believes that his thoughts are being shared with others, while *thought echo* is the experience that his own thoughts are being repeated or echoed with little interval between thought and echo.

Passivity experiences

Other passivity experiences or behaviour due to external forces or influences include sudden rages or depressions leading to withdrawal. Philip strongly demonstrates these frightening phenomena well, for his mother describes periods when he became enraged, as well as other periods of withdrawal when he retreated to bed, and no amount of persuasion or demand would cause him to get up. Such times cause great frustration both for patient and carer, and would in time enhance the conflict between them. Here Mrs Moate depicts the first phases of such a painful conflict between carer and patient. When Philip recovered from the acute phase of withdrawal, he would then exhibit excessive affection towards his mother, as if he knew that he had been particularly trying.

Emotional disturbance

It is known that emotional disturbance also occurs in schizophrenia. In some cases mood changes are prominent, though they do not carry great diagnostic weight. The more severe the schizophrenia, the more incongruous the patient's emotional response—such as uncontrollable laughter in the face of tragedy. But even when there is not this extreme mood change, there may well be a flattening of affect of mood: that is, the patient is cool, detached, and there is a lack of response which prevents the establishment of any warm relationship or rapport.

Severe anxiety or depression may sometimes be superimposed on the basic schizophrenic illness. Significant depression occurs in 10% of schizophrenics, though there is some doubt whether this is an inherent part of the illness or a reaction to it. Again, sometimes episodes of great excitement with overactivity may occur.

Motor disorder

Abnormal movements and posture may occur; for example the patient may exhibit an eccentric posture like holding his arm aloft for hours for no purpose. He may also continually repeat movement of his arm or leg for no apparent purpose.

Negative symptoms

Negative symptoms are deficits of personality and behaviour. The key word to describe them is 'lack', for there is lack of initiative, lack of energy, lack of interest and lack of emotional response. These symptoms have increasingly come to be accepted as an inherent part of the schizophrenic process. They may occur insidiously or persist after an acute, severe episode of the illness. When the patient presents with a preponderance of negative symptoms, a detailed history will usually reveal such an acute episode.

Negative symptoms, then, mean the absence of normal features of behaviour. They have definite prognostic implications, for their presence makes rehabilitation more difficult, with a tendency for the patient to lack drive; this in turn leads to social isolation and general apathy. Again, this in turn leads to further deterioration and personal self-neglect, including neglect of hygiene. This deterioration occurs equally in the streets of the inner cities as in the back wards of large mental hospitals.

During one phase of his illness, Philip exhibited such negative symptoms with a lack of interest, which led in turn to social withdrawal and isolation, a source of tremendous frustration within the family, and one which further produced feelings of anger. It is interesting that withdrawal was a mechanism used by Philip on two major occasions in his life when he was unable to meet the stresses of the hour. During his school day, when he was not able to keep up with his studies, he played truant, although even his masters then realised that this truancy was 'different from the ordinary one'.[1] In fact this withdrawal arose from difficulties in his schoolwork. These in turn were probably caused by difficulties in concentrating and an understandable inability to face the humiliating failure. Later, faced with his own active symptoms of schizophrenia, he was unable to cope and withdrew, isolated himself and stayed in bed. The family on both occasions might well have thought that he was being hysterical or difficult for the sake of drawing attention to himself. In fact, however, this was Philip's way of dealing with the real difficulties within his personality—which eventually blossomed into a full-blown schizophrenic illness.

How is schizophrenia diagnosed?

The presence of positive symptoms such as primary delusions, third-person auditory hallucinations, thought and motor disorder in the absence of an organic brain condition would all lead to the diagnosis of schizophrenia. Most European psychiatrists would agree that diagnosis could be made on such a basis. If the patient shows negative symptoms only initially, then a history of a previous acute schizophrenic

---

[1] See page 39.

episode would confirm the diagnosis. If there is no such clear-cut history, the diagnosis would depend on whether there is evidence of a slow deterioration in social performance and a failure to achieve expected levels of success and competence.

Then these symptoms or cluster of symptoms occurring together are highly suggestive of the diagnosis schizophrenia, although there are no specific diagnostic tests. Diagnosis rests on a characteristic history, usually from a close relative who has noticed a marked change in the person, and on the clinical acumen of the physician. Schizophrenics often deny that there is anything wrong with them because they have no insight into their illness. But this lack of insight only illustrates the severity of the illness, and explains how difficult it is to get their co-operation.

The description of these symptoms makes clear how frightening they are. Indeed there is little so frightening as seeing a person approaching a psychotic breakdown when one witnesses disintegration of personality and the production of these very strange symptoms and phenomena. This is true for an experienced physician in the field and thus must be even more powerfully true for relatives witnessing them for the very first time in their own dear flesh and blood. Hence the relief of a firm diagnosis given by an expert because it does, though only partically, explain the disturbed behaviour of the patient, in particular the gross change from apparent normality to a disturbed psychotic state.

During her account, in summing up this change, Mrs Moate says that though she continued to love Philip and to care for him (and indeed did so to the end), she felt that after the psychotic change Philip was no longer the same person. In a manner of speaking she is correct, for a fundamental change occurs in the person; and his or her relatives and carers have to learn anew how to relate to him. As a physician I have observed how great is the suffering of some patients when they develop delusions and hallucinations.

They become preoccupied with them, withdrawn, and unable to carry on with their day-to-day affairs; inevitably, further frustration, irritability and even anger follow.

Seeing how frightful and anxiety-producing this change can be, doctors and others of the caring professions must face again the great need for special sensitivity towards both patient and carer. No doubt some relatives, angered by the fact that they are the victims of such a condition, would project their anger onto the professionals. However, professionals need to reassure and support rather than increase the conflict.

In this respect again, it is important to note that the extended family or neighbours and friends and members of one's church will be faced with a similar dilemma. Of course they too would be frightened about facing the unknown, an illness that is not readily acceptable to society as a whole, and might then withdraw their support. Yet ironically it is at this very time that the patient and the carers need their support.

3

What is the Cause of Schizophrenia?

No single cause has been established for schizophrenia, and the condition probably results from the interaction of several factors.

Genetic and hereditary factors

As stated earlier, the lifetime risk of developing schizophrenia is approximately 1% in the general population, while the risk is much higher in relatives of sufferers. For example, children with one schizophrenic parent stand 12% risk, while those with two affected parents have a 36% risk.

Studies of the frequency of the development of the illness in affected identical twins have shown that in 86% of such pairs both twins are affected, and significantly, this result is similar whether the twins are reared together or are apart from birth.

The precise mode of the genetic transmission from parent to child is not however known, but most experts agree that what is inherited is not a certainty of developing the disease but an increased vulnerability to the condition. Indeed 60% of sufferers give no family history of the disease.

Intensive research continues in this field in the belief that more will soon be revealed about the genetic component among the causes of schizophrenia. But although there is a strong indication that there *is* a genetic component, it is also clear that inheritance alone cannot be a complete explanation for the illness.

Biochemical abnormalities

For around forty years there has been a notion, varying in intensity at different periods, that schizophrenia might have a biochemical basis; but no consistent biochemical substance has been isolated from the brain of sufferers. Such a theory arose from the fact that the well-known drug amphetamine, and other similar substances, could produce schizophrenic-like symptoms. It was thus considered that if such a substance or a derivative was found in the brain of schizophrenics, this would be the cause of the condition.

Various researchers claimed that such substances were isolated from the brains of schizophrenics, but this finding has not been consistent. The theory was given new impetus when it was found that many of the drugs which removed the major symptoms of schizophrenia, including delusions and hallucinations, acted by blocking a substance in the brain known as *dopamine*, which is released by amphetamines. Various researchers claimed that they had isolated this specific substance or toxin, but the findings were inconsistent and could not be repeated at other centres. Indeed it has been proved impossible to isolate a specific toxin from the brains of schizophrenics, and many of the findings of the early biochemical investigations turned out to be the result of unusual diet or medication.

Other possible physical causes

Neurological abnormalities are often detected in schizophrenic patients, although (as I have mentioned) intensive investigations have failed to find any obvious change in the brain that is detectable with the naked eye. The neurological signs are minor ones, vary from patient to patient, and do not indicate that any specific part of the brain is affected.

Recently, advanced investigations using computerised analysis and invoked potentials with EEG (electroencephalogram testing) confirmed that there were more abnormalities among schizophrenics than among normal subjects; but these studies have not pointed to a single abnormality consistently present in all patients.

The introduction of CT scanning (a special, advanced X-ray method) has provided a non-invasive method for investigating the brain size of schizophrenic patients. It was reported that the ventricles (ie the spaces within the brain) were significantly larger in schizophrenics, suggesting that there may well be a shrinkage of some brain tissue in schizophrenics.

The full significance of this physical finding cannot be fully assessed without further research. At present one can simply assert that neurological signs which do not locate any physical lesion do occur more frequently in schizophrenics than among the normal population, and that there may be a shrinkage of the brain tissue. These findings are important in suggesting that schizophrenia is a physical illness.

Recently it has also been suggested that viral infections may be a cause of schizophrenia and that virus-like material can be found and isolated from the cerebro-spinal fluid (ie the fluid surrounding the brain and spinal cord). However, confirmation or otherwise from further research is crucial.

Psychological causes

These psychological causes include psychological factors of the individual patient, interpersonal relationships within the family, and social factors.

Psychodynamic and psychoanalytic theories have attributed schizophrenia to the effects of traumatic experiences in early childhood. They have viewed its symptoms as a regression to a very early stage in personality development. Under stress, during teenage or adulthood, the schizophrenic will revert to infantile behaviour. While these psycho-dynamic theories do explain well the bizarre, infantile behaviour of the schizophrenic, they do not explain how and why the illness occurred in the first place.

Family stresses have been increasingly suggested as a relevant cause of the onset of schizophrenia. In the 1940s the harsh concept of the 'schizophrenogenic mother' was put forward, when it was considered that the mothers of schizophrenics themselves constituted a potent factor in the cause of the illness. This theory was based on the consideration that these mothers showed excessive psychological abnormalities. A disordered communication between the mother and the schizophrenic was supposedly based on the 'double bind' phenomenon. This means that when one instruction is given overtly, it is contradicted by a covert instruction. For example, a mother may command a child to come to her, while at the very same time conveying by her manner and tone of voice that she does not wish him to do so. A further distressing element here is that there is no escape from the bind.

Others have suggested different patterns of disordered communication within the family, but there is no conclusive evidence that any such communication problems are causal, and researchers in this field should allow the possibility that the abnormalities noted are a reaction to, rather than the cause of schizophrenia. (And here it is important to note that theories of disordered communications within families of schizophrenics can give no satisfactory explanation for why it is unusual for more than one child in such a family to develop schizophrenia.)

At the same time, distinguished researchers during the past twenty years have shown clearly that the disease is exacerbated by unsatisfactory home and family relationships, especially when there is what is termed 'high expressed emotion' families—where the family atmosphere is hostile and critical towards the patient, and where there is more than thirty-five hours-a-week contact between the person and his family. Even if the high emotional expression is of too much *warmth* (particularly of a possessive kind), it may be equally harmful.

Environmental stress

It is now known that life events which most people usually take in their stride are a particular source of stress for the schizophrenic. These life events such as moving house, changing jobs, illness, injury, loss of a family member or a friend through moving or death can precipitate the onset of an acute episode of schizophrenia in susceptible individuals, or a relapse in a pre-existing condition.

We will turn now to an examination of the social setting of the schizophrenic, including care for his family and the use of specialised drugs.

4

Treatment and Management

Although we do not know the precise causes of schizophrenia, we have established from Mrs Moate's account and
from the previous chapter that many facts regarding schizophrenia *are* known. In the first place it is an illness that causes
massive suffering to the patient as well as to the relatives and
carers. If—as it frequently is—it is progressive, it can cause
marked deterioration in the young person so that his academic work and other achievements are reduced considerably from his first potential. Tremendous suffering and
despondency within the patient follow.

The very nature of the change initially causes shock, fear,
resentment—and subsequently anger—within the relatives
or carers. But in emphasising the familial factors in the
production of the illness, the clinician only adds distress to
both patient and carer. Often in the past doctors might well
have been accused (in our eagerness to state the theories of
the schizophrenogenic mother and of family discord) of
merely adding fuel to the fire of conflict. Indeed, as we have
seen, it is not certain whether schizophrenia causes the family
conflict, or the family conflict causes the illness.

The great probability is that schizophrenia is primarily a
physical illness, albeit with a metabolic dysfunction as a
basis, which, because of the symptoms—including the

change in personality and behaviour—causes great strain within families. Understandably, carers then react with frustration, irritation, anger, and these feelings exacerbate the symptoms as well as aggravating the strained relationship between carer and patient. This situation leads me to emphasise that one outstanding feature of the management and treatment of schizophrenia and the carers is the relief of tension, conflict and suffering. This means (again) that the earlier the diagnosis is made, and the earlier that everyone is put into the picture, the better for all concerned. Management of the whole social situation is thus imperative.

Building the relationship

At the very onset, once the diagnosis is firmly established, there must be counselling of both patient and carer. It is essential that the psychiatrist be frank with the patient about his condition. How much the patient should be told about his diagnosis and illness with all its implications, would take into account many factors including the severity of the illness and the symptoms, the degree of insight the patient has, and the views of the relatives. The telling must be done in such a way as to minimalise any feelings of fear, distress and hopelessness. If the patient asks pertinent questions about his condition and his future, then details should be given if the psychiatrist feels that these are appropriate. I must state that the evidence given to me proves that psychiatrists often do not give the information to enough people at the time that they request it. Thus carers and patients remain in ignorance of the illness, particularly of what to expect in the future. Their distress and anger increase; whereas information usually reduces fear and increases compliance from the patient and support from the relatives.

It must be admitted that some patients and even relatives would react differently if informed of the true condition of the patient. They may well become angry initially and project that anger onto the psychiatrist and those looking after the patient; this feeling may persist for a long time. (The carers may blame the psychiatrist for the production of the illness just as we blame the TV weathermen for the poor summers we now have in the United Kingdom!) Thus counselling, which should include advice and general strategies for the patient, should be given with considerable sensitivity to his needs.

Success in management depends on establishing a good relationship with the patient from the very beginning so that his co-operation is enlisted. It may be difficult to establish such a good working relationship, especially with chronic patients who are markedly paranoid or emotionally unresponsive. But with skill and patience, progress is usually made. At the same time, a good relationship must also be established with the carer or relative, especially if the patient remains at home or in the community, or will return there after a short period in hospital.

Helping the family

With increasing care of patients in the community, difficulties within the families have been accentuated. One group finds difficulty because of social withdrawal, as occurred with Philip. At that time they fail to communicate with other members of the family, lack spontaneous speech, have few interests, and neglect themselves.

Another group—of more obviously disturbed and socially embarrassing patients—exhibits restlessness or uninhibited social behaviour and threats of violence. Relatives of this second group often feel anxious and depressed as well as bewildered, guilty and angry. They are uncertain about how to deal with the difficult and odd behaviour. The lack of sympathy and understanding from the members of their family, neighbours and members of the church only accentuates the difficulties and isolates them further. Just as the friends of the schizophrenic himself tend to desert him, often at the instigation of their families, the carers and relatives of the schizophrenic also feel that they are looked at as contaminated. Hence further isolation occurs between them and their friends. This happens just at the time when they are most in need of active support in dealing with their disturbed child. This unfortunate result of the illness in Philip's case is very well delineated by his mother. Mrs Moate obviously felt acutely the isolation which the illness brought about for Philip, and also despaired sometimes of the isolation between her family and the rest of the world around.

The role of the church

In this respect we must be particularly concerned about the lack of support given specifically by Christians and members of Christian churches. Several parents have told me that when their son or daughter developed schizophrenia, members of the church gave no support; in fact they often became hostile and discontinued the past friendship.

Herein lies a considerable challenge for the church today. One has often wondered at the fact that the central theme of the Christian gospel is love; yet though mental illness is a sphere of human life where there is a greater need for such love than in almost any other, so little has been shown. Christians who might have an aptitude for helping the mentally ill need to be actively involved, in particular with psychotics such as schizophrenics.

Groups of befrienders could be set up within fellowships to give active support to families and schizophrenics, both during acute phases and if the case becomes chronic so that deterioration in academic achievement occurs. We live in a competitive world, and when a boy who would have achieved much academically suddenly begins to deteriorate, hopes for further advancement recede. At this point active support held up by members of a fellowship is indispensable.

Again, it is a terrible indictment of Christians that when

families are suddenly told that they have a schizophrenic son or daughter, they are more frightened of informing their Christian friends than others. They seem to feel guilt that they have 'produced' such a person. This is linked with the general fear of madness and the fact that Christians feel very guilty if they break down emotionally or mentally in any way. This is even more true in an illness as severe as schizophrenia.

This mixture of fear and guilt is further compounded by the fact that often some parts of the church might suggest that the illness is devil possession and that exorcism is the order of the day. They seem to suggest that the New Testament gives this impression of all such illnesses. However, there is nothing in the New Testament to suggest that schizophrenia was regarded as devil possession. The medical situation at present is clear: if someone is diagnosed as suffering from schizophrenia, he is regarded as suffering from a psychotic illness which needs definite medical treatment. Of course, this does not rule out the possibility, as is true in any illness, of spiritual healing through God's direct intervention.

The treatments doctors have in their armament today are God-given. They may have emerged from human research but are in fact discoveries from God's world. Even the drugs, which in a remarkable way were found to remove such ferocious symptoms as delusions and hallucinations, are derived from the natural and created world. Thus Christians need not have any guilt about the use of drugs, especially if they look upon them in this way. I am aware, through correspondence and discussions with many Christians, that some do indeed find it difficult to accept that healing does include drug therapy; spiritual healing and drugs are not mutually exclusive but can go hand in hand, working in effective and practical ways.

An example of healing and drugs working together is that of diabetes mellitus, which has a biochemical basis. The patient needs insulin for the rest of his life, usually by injection, as a form of substitution therapy for something lacking in the body. Hardly anyone would expect a diabetic to do without his insulin, although healing does go beyond mere insulin therapy. Why should we therefore treat the schizophrenic differently?

Drug therapy and social care

This discussion leads me to look at drug therapy in detail. Before the 1950s there were no specific drugs for schizophrenia. We remember that paraldehyde was used in vast quantities as a form of sedation, but it was suddenly found that the drug reserpine was effective in removing some schizophrenic symptoms. Later, in the 1950s, came the remarkable discovery of Largactil (Chlorpromazine), the first of the neuroleptics (or so-called major tranquillizers) found to have anti-psychotic properties and to be able to remove delusions and hallucinations. In a large mental hospital it was remarkable to see this drug prescribed to one side of the hospital and not to the other. A controlled large-scale experiment occurred before my very eyes. The countless reports of the next few years merely confirmed what I had seen myself—great numbers of chronic schizophrenics and new admissions were responding to Largactil and other newer major tranquillizers. It was nothing short of a miracle—a revolutionary new treatment on the same scale as the advent of antibiotics. Not surprisingly, in the first flush of enthusiasm, we believed that all patients might respond to these drugs. Later enthusiasm was tempered when we realised that this was not so.

Of acute schizophrenic cases, 25% recover spontaneously. There are therefore good grounds for withholding the drugs initially, especially on the first admission, in order to assess the prognosis clearly in an individual case. Of those needing drugs, about 65% improve markedly, although they may suffer occasional acute relapses. About 10% do not respond to drugs and remain disabled to varying degrees.

Anti-depressant drugs are sometimes given to schizophrenics for depressive symptoms which do occur in schizophrenia and often remain when the florid psychotic symptoms have responded to neuroleptic medication. However, since it is not easy to distinguish between depressive symptoms and apathy, it is difficult to assess the effects of anti-depressant medication in chronic schizophrenia.

An overwhelming case can thus be made for the prescribing of drugs to the schizophrenic, especially in the acute phase, and then subsequently for giving a maintenance dose of the drug. Paradoxically, those with acute onset and quite severe symptoms may well have a good prognosis, while those with chronic negative systems of apathy and lack of interest may well have a poor prognosis. Those with a positive family history of schizophrenia carry a worse prognosis; whereas those with an accompanied mood disorder often do well.

Often it is better to give medication by injection, since some patients fail to take oral medication regularly over long periods. The dosage, which should be the minimum required to suppress symptoms, can be determined by cautiously varying its size and frequency on observing the patient's clinical state. Some patients show little response to anti-psychotic medication. For such cases it should not be given continuously but only for acute relapses. It is uncertain for how long prophylactic medication should be continued, but the treatment should be reviewed at least every three or four months and side effects assessed. A balance should be struck between benefits and adverse effects.

Major tranquillisers

Anti-psychotic drugs which are used in schizophrenia are known as neuroleptics or major tranquillisers and can be classified into four main groups: *phenothiazines, butyrophenones, thioxanthenes* and *diphenylbutylpiperidines*. The first and most famous of these drugs was the phenothiazine called *chlorpromazine (largactil)*.

Introduced in the last thirty-five years, these powerfully effective anti-psychotic drugs have thus revolutionised the treatment of schizophrenia and enabled many sufferers to lead a reasonable life in the community. Previously they would have become long-stay hospital patients, with no hope of ever living a full life in the community. In the process, they would lose all hope of such an existence and would become thoroughly institutionalised—apathetic, never expecting to improve or leave the institution.

The main direct uses of these major tranquillisers are to reduce if not remove hallucinations, delusions, agitation and psychomotor excitement (physical restlessness). They are believed to act by blocking the receptors of the substance dopamine, which (as described in Chapter 3) is a naturally occurring substance in the brain. Unfortunately, these drugs do have unwanted side-effects such as stiffness and tremor; and as these are dose-related, it is important to keep the dosage as low as possible.

The drugs are usually given by mouth, especially initially, during the first attack of the illness. However, because the injectable form of the drug can be given intramuscularly, they act more effectively and may thus be given in this form in an acute or severe attack of the illness. As already described, however, drug treatment is in most cases begun by the oral route; usually improvement is noted within five to seven days, though not fully established for several weeks.

As schizophrenia is often recurrent or a chronic condition, maintenance during therapy is often necessary, usually in lower dosages. The development of *depot* injections (ie a long-acting injectable form of the drugs Modecate and Clopixol) now allows the treatment to be given at longer intervals such as one to four weeks and also ensures that the patient has indeed had the drug for that period. This is important, because it is well known that lack of co-operation with the treatment is one major cause of relapse.

There is no proven way of distinguishing patients who require medication to improve from those who have improved without medication. In the last twenty years many controlled trials have shown the effectiveness of continued oral and depot therapy in preventing relapse. Again, there has been no success in predicting which patients benefit from such treatment. Since extended anti-psychotic medication may lead to irreversible dyskinesis (ie involuntary facial movements), it is important to know how long such treatment is to be given, though there is no clear answer to this question. It has, however, been reported that over a three-year maintenance period anti-psychotic medication is three times better than the placebo in preventing relapse. Though there is a widespread clinical impression that depot injections are more successful than continued oral medication in preventing relapses of schizophrenia, this has not been proved by research.

It is essential to emphasise that these anti-psychotic drugs are not given in isolation. The patient does not merely come to the clinic to get a needle into a part of his body with no words spoken! Rather it is essential to build up a therapeutic environment either in out-patients or in the home. At out-patients he or she will meet at least the same nurses—and perhaps social workers—regularly, as well as a doctor, albeit usually a junior one. In this respect it is important to have continuity of care.

I was struck when one of our auxiliary nurses who had been in the clinic for many years was transferred elsewhere. She turned to me and said that she hoped that 'my boys' would now be well looked after. They had made a relationship with her, and she had got to know them well as they came for their injections. Such relationships could equally well be established at home, where an effective, conscientious community psychiatric nurse will create a therapeutic relationship and be accepted by the patient, even though he may be very ill and with acute, overt symptoms.

I have been impressed by observing how some such ill patients readily welcome the community psychiatric nurse into their homes and allow him or her to give them the injections. This effective working relationship has been built up over the months and the years, so that the community psychiatric nurse is therefore involved both in the giving of medication and in social case work. In addition, the team looking after the patient should also involve a social worker, for it is known that social case work alone has only a small effect in reducing relapse, but combined with medication, it has a significant effect. The difference may occur partly because patients take their drugs more regularly when seen by social workers and community psychiatric nurses, but such an arrangement seems unlikely to be the whole explanation.

Other physical treatments

Much discussion goes on about the role of electroconvulsive therapy (ECT) in the treatment of schizophrenia. It is fair to say that it is accepted that the traditional indications for ECT are catatonic state and severe depressive symptoms accompanying schizophrenia. In both these conditions the effects of ECT can often be rapid and striking. Nowadays ECT is seldom used for other presentations of schizophrenia, although in acute episodes where there is marked behaviour disturbance there is evidence that it can be rapidly effective.

The role of psychotherapy

Individual psychotherapy aiming to find the past hurts was used quite commonly for schizophrenics in the United States but does not appear to have been successful, and indeed there is some danger in its causing over-stimulation and consequently relapse. Many kinds of group therapy have been tried but have been found to be of little benefit in acute schizophrenia. If however we accept 'supportive psychotherapy' as meaning a form of treatment during which the patient can make relationships with doctor, nurse or social worker, can discuss his problems and share his thoughts on a superficial level—then psychotherapy can not only be effective but an important part in building up the therapeutic atmosphere described earlier. This is true whether within the hospital out-patients, day hospital or community. Such supportive psychotherapy is valuable in psychiatric patients such as the chronic schizophrenic, who may be severely handicapped both emotionally and in his interpersonal relationships, and in whom there may well be no prospect of basic improvement. Relatives, friends and carers who may give social support will themselves need continual support, for they may not be able to cope completely with the needs of the patient. I will describe this form of supportive psychotherapy in greater detail in Chapter 5.

Prognosis in schizophrenia

Although it is often believed that the outcome of schizophrenia is usually worse than that of most mental illnesses, there has been an undoubted improvement in its possible outcome since the mid 1950s. Why? Certainly the advent of major tranquillisers has been helpful, together with a new optimistic, more caring attitude and improved social management—both within and without large mental hospitals.

Although the exciting hopes for the effectiveness of drug treatment and prognosis have not been fully realised, improved prognosis in this illness *has* been sustained, and patients now have still more hope of recovering from an acute episode; they also have the real possibility of successful return to a useful life.

It must be clearly understood by all who deal with schizophrenic patients that—following an acute episode of schizophrenia—one third of young adults will make a complete recovery without specific treatment (although they may be subject to isolated, acute relapses in response to stress). But in general they do well, and their progress and prognosis are encouraging.

Another third will respond and be relieved by treatment including drugs, although they will have more episodes of breakdown under conditions of stress. Patients in this group can however be rehabilitated to live reasonable but perhaps sheltered lives in the community. They can frequently undertake employment, though not necessarily at the same level of responsibility as that they could maintain previously.

In spite of treatment, including drugs, the remaining third of patients will progress to a chronic state and will need continual surveillance and support of varying degrees. Some will need long-term, closely supervised sheltered accommodation. This group usually has a poor educational and social background, being isolated and without family support; and the onset of their schizophrenia is often gradual and insidious, with emotional withdrawal, flatness and lack of drive.

Surprisingly, a sudden, severe attack with obvious delusions and hallucinations and considerable disorder of thought, may well clear up quickly and completely. If there is an associated disordered mood, such as depression, these cases often do well. If, however, there is a strong history of schizophrenia in the family, the prognosis is worse.

Certainly, early diagnosis, direction and appropriate treatment, including properly prescribed drugs and good social support/management, all make for a better outcome.

5

General Care

Early care

As we saw in Chapter 1, the first important feature of the
initial management of a schizophrenic patient is the establishment of prompt, accurate diagnosis. (Philip's story is a salu-
tary lesson to all concerned in this field.) As stated, the
assessment begins with a differential diagnosis, which is
particularly concerned with the exclusion of organic disorder, especially of a drug-induced state, mood disorder and
personality disorder. And because it may be difficult in
practice to elicit all the symptoms from a withdrawn or
suspicious patient, it may be necessary to have several psychiatric interviews. It may also be necessary to draw on the
help of a close relative, who will be able to give a more
complete history of the patient's previous personality, noting
important matter of any change in behaviour, work record,
accommodation and leisure pursuits, as well as his past medical and psychiatric history.

The social worker, too, should be brought in early on to
make contact with the relatives; although it is equally essential that the key relative involved in caregiving has easy and
early access to the doctor. Thus begins the build-up of the
therapeutic milieu I have so far emphasised.

In most cases where the disorder is suspected, hospitalisation may well be desired for this first essential assessment; and certainly, in all cases, psychiatric opinion is essential. Further acute psychiatric episodes may also result in admission into hospital, preferably early rather than late. Particularly with the emphasis on a shift into the community, one of the dangers is that there might be insufficient beds available or prevalent attitudes militating against admission.

Already it is clear that there is an outcry from relatives and carers who have had difficulties in getting help for schizophrenics who do relapse. One cannot over-emphasise, then, that in the present changing situation it is essential that facilities be available immediately for the assessment and appropriate management of all schizophrenics who experience an acute worsening of symptoms.

The very least that can be done in this situation is to see the patient immediately, to re-assess the care and to bear in mind the burden of the families. It is useless and unfair to criticise the families, because by and large they have been prepared to take tremendous burdens with little complaint. They do, however, become understandably fearful, as well as having feelings of helplessness and hopelessness, when their sons and daughters again begin to show worsening of overt schizophrenic symptoms. Superficial reassurance from a doctor or nurse at that point is completely inadequate to allay the fears and feelings of despondency, and early response from the professionals in fact reduces the suffering of the patient and the relatives, which is certainly considerable.

In emphasising this prompt response I am aware that, as stated earlier, there are groups of people (including ex-patients) who vehemently oppose any form of admission, be it informally or compulsorily, into any psychiatric units or mental hospitals. The conflict is intensified because the patient lacks insight and does not appreciate being examined and questioned, let alone being admitted into a psychiatric unit. The vast body of public and professional opinion is however that a patient with the probable diagnosis of schizophrenia needs to be admitted into hospital for assessment, whether for the first time or during subsequent relapses. While he is in hospital, the doctor will have the opportunity of examining him, perhaps gathering (with the help of a social worker) full personal and past history, and making contact with the relatives and carers. At the same time, nurses will be able to carry out careful observations of the patients; these are invaluable in clinching the diagnosis.

During this period of close contact between professional and patient, and between professionals and relatives, a good therapeutic relationship should be built up with the patient and the relatives. It must be admitted that to establish such a good working relationship with patients in the acute phase, or even with chronic patients, needs skill and patience—but it can usually be achieved. The patient and relatives should be given information about schizophrenia, and regular discussions with both should ensure that questions regarding the illness are answered. Any anxieties about the illness and its prognosis and future management should be discussed in detail.

At this time there should also be discussions about the plan of social management. There would be an initial observation period of about two or three weeks without any medication unless the patient becomes violent, or unless he is likely to abscond, or becomes overtly distressed. Consideration should then be given as to whether medication should be prescribed or not. If it is—as in most cases—then how to begin, when to administer and in what doses will be considered according to the patient's condition and progress. Even at this point relatives will have many questions regarding medication. Often they ask what effects it will have on the patient: will it cause harm to his brain? will he need drugs forever? At this point some Christians feel aggrieved that their sons or daughters have to be prescribed drugs, believing that they should be able to cope with all stress and breakdowns without recourse to drugs. In this respect education of the family, community and even the church can be of help.

I make this emphasis because of the vast numbers of Christians who have written and 'phoned me personally about drugs. In the end, they have generally accepted reassurance and allowed their relatives to be prescribed drugs, usually with good consequences. Here I reiterate something I wrote in *Healing the Hurt Mind*, because it has proved helpful to so many people: that if my own dear son had been unfortunate enough to have suffered from schizophrenia, there would have been two things I would have expected in his care. Firstly, to choose the best psychiatrist I know (I am not prepared to name anybody because I want to remain friends with all my colleagues!) and, secondly, to expect him or her to prescribe appropriate anti-psychotic medication as soon as possible and then to maintain him on it as long as necessary.

Admission

Although I have emphasised that relatives today complain about the lack of quick, effective response to acute schizophrenic episodes, others have revealed the opposite fear: that if their relatives are admitted too quickly into a psychiatric unit or mental hospital, there may be the prospect of a life-sentence of hospitalisation. Certainly, in the past, such patients did too frequently degenerate slowly in the chronic wards of mental hospitals, forgotten by the whole world and incapacitated more and more by their deterioration until death—sometimes as much as half a century or more later—mercifully relieved them of the final stages of their illness. This fear became one of the most important and pertinent reasons for the shift from hospitals of that kind to care in the community.

But hospitalisation is merely an incident in the proper management of the patient. A hospital, after all, is surely a part of the community which is used at a critical stage of the illness. It allows asylum for the patient, where he can be treated with dignity and allowed to express himself. It also brings relief for relatives, giving them an opportunity to take stock of the situation. It is also a place of opportunity to observe and gather information, in particular to note the behaviour of the patient and establish the need for medication; any additional examinations or investigations can be carried out at the same time.

In the ward, the patient should be allowed to get used to his new environment gradually, without undue pressure. My experience is that the nurses are remarkably good at making patients feel at ease—even the most disturbed. Joining various ward groups for discussion should occur gradually, as should occupational therapy, where gentle introduction of structured activity can benefit the patient. Very disturbed schizophrenics, however, sometimes find it difficult to join in with others or even to concentrate for short periods.

When improvement does occur, an active rehabilitation plan must be established. Rehabilitation begins from the first day in a hospital, not on the day prior to the patient's discharge! While in the hospital the patient will take time to settle in and to understand the hospital regime. When the acute symptoms have receded, usually following treatment with drugs, the schizophrenic will be encouraged to take part in activities on the ward. He will then be encouraged to do simple tasks by the nurses and/or occupational therapists: on the ward initially, and later in the occupational therapy room or department. In this way the rehabilitation process begins. It is hoped that this will continue after discharge from hospital with attendance at a day hospital or day centre.

Discharge

Discharge can take many forms. It may occur after several weekends or short periods at home. Sometimes it may be better to place the patient elsewhere in temporary hostel accommodation. After the final discharge from the in-patient unit, it may be advisable for the patient to attend a day hospital or day centre. At the same time it is important to plan appropriate leisure activities. It is essential too that the relatives and carers be brought into all the discussions, so that they may be fully informed and any queries or fears again discussed fully. For the vast majority of patients it will be necessary to continue maintenance medication, which must be organised and monitored, preferably by visits from the community nurse or by attendance at a clinic, where injections will be given.

In this respect it must be remembered that about 30% of patients themselves will discontinue medication. There should thus be out-patient follow-up when the patient comes to the clinic at regular intervals, preferably to the same clinic and to the same doctor for the appropriate period.

If improvement is maintained, the intervals can be extended. But if the patient misses an out-patient appointment, the social worker or community psychiatric nurse should make enquiries. Often the reason for absence is that there has been a deterioration in the patient's condition; he has become more withdrawn and negativistic. Hence a short period of admission must be considered.

Community psychiatric nurses and social workers as well as relatives can give information about the deterioration in the patient. Relatives are usually the best informants because they live with the patient twenty-four hours a day, but they need to be treated sensitively, and their account of a relapse or an acute crisis must be taken seriously. (Two professional women told me that they were even frightened of telling doctors that such a relapse had taken place because they were afraid that they would be blamed.) Generally the parents of schizophrenics carry big burdens and do not really complain unnecessarily. Hence a swift decision to readmit the patient in such circumstances can usually be effective in bringing about rapid control of symptoms. This decisiveness in turn preserves a good relationship between relatives and professionals.

In order to avoid relapse and the need for readmission, the patient should be counselled over many matters, including their potential social difficulties and their own ability to manage themselves generally. If the patient so wishes, it is advisable to give him as many details of the illness as possible and its possible effects. He should be advised on general facts, for example that stress tends to precipitate the recurrence of florid symptoms; thus he is well advised to avoid all demanding situations, be they occupational or emotional relationships. If he has responded well to medication, it must be emphasised that he should not reduce or discontinue the drug without full discussion with his doctor. Again, he can be advised that if there is a worsening of his condition, when his acute florid symptoms return, an increased dose can quickly bring about an improvement.

In chronic schizophrenics the danger is often under-stimulation and a tendency to isolate themselves. In this way they under-achieve—even allowing for the 'scarring' that occurs as a result of the illness. By contrast, it is encouraging to note that some who have suffered severe schizophrenic symptoms have, while on medication, even been successful in gaining high class honours degrees. A few have sat these examinations while being in-patients. However, in general, patients should be advised to resume social and occupational activities step by step, not over-reaching themselves. They then minimise the danger of failure, and their confidence is restored.

Schizophrenia and the family

When the care of schizophrenic patients is increasingly undertaken within the family circle, it is imperative that advice to, support for—and not infrequently treatment of—other members of the family be considered highly important aspects of general management. As strikingly exhibited by Mrs Moate, responsibility for the schizophrenic may at times be demanding in the extreme, even for the most robust. Relatives are often subjected to social, economic and emotional strains which at times seem scarcely tolerable.

Here, Mary Moate's words in countering the viewpoint that schizophrenia is not an illness but a mere opting out are illuminating. Referring to the professionals, she states,

> Schizophrenia from a clinical, detached, distanced
> viewpoint is one thing, but we were experiencing it at its
> very worst—at first hand! Anyone who has lived with
> or experienced mental illness at such close proximity will
> realise the full horror of it. . . . We had no doubts at all
> that Philip was desperately ill.[1]

It would surely not be surprising if other such families wished to retreat from the situation. Often I have wondered why they have not. For, of such patients, well over half return to their elderly parents or other relatives; only one in three goes to live-in lodgings or similar accommodation. Thus the recent improvement in the outcome of schizophrenia, especially from therapeutic advances, has resulted in increased and enormous burdens on these relatives. Again I ask, why do so many relatives of schizophrenic patients remain so devoted? They are on duty all the time without option and may find themselves in frightening and frightful situations, which in turn cause further guilt. They accept the initial disturbance because they still have hope, but when

---

[1] See page 55.

they experience a repetition time and time again of a relapse, they become despondent and desperate. They are frightened of the kind of acute symptoms during which they themselves may sometimes be caught up in the delusions.

They tend to worry even more about the persistent traits of personality associated with the negative symptoms of the disease: further withdrawal, apathy, laziness and unsociability. Yet still they hope; still they support. It is clear sometimes on close questioning, however, that where a family is highly charged emotionally, separation would perhaps be best. There are nevertheless others who, in spite of the deterioration of the clinical state, remain supportive. Thus time spent with relatives is of great importance both to the patient and to relatives. Such time will deflect the fear that the professionals do not appreciate their difficulties; that the professionals assume they are merely complaining for the sake of complaining and are evading their own responsibilities.

Shared responsibilities should be the order of the day, and at various times and at various stages of the illness the carer will take most of the responsibility—sometimes the social worker, sometimes the community psychiatric nurse or the doctor, sometimes the relative. As the illness progresses, or with subsequent relapses, more time should be spent in explaining the nature and process of schizophrenia, perhaps emphasising the role of the negative symptoms they so bitterly complain of. Of course this means that relatives concerned with the management of the schizophrenic patient must be seen at regular intervals, and it is important to look for the early stages of anxiety and depression in the relatives and to give appropriate advice. The relatives' level of knowledge and accompanying attitudes should be noted. These may change significantly with the provision of corrective information and with the opportunity for them to express their feelings, even of anger.

Mrs Moate obviously noted symptoms in detail and interpreted them. On one occasion she records her belief that whereas the patient's withdrawal into himself can cause the relatives great strain and stress, the patient himself may then be protected by the very nature of his symptoms. Sadly, this is not the case, for even when patients appear to be withdrawn and uncommunicative with no outward, overt, active symptoms, they are still suffering a great inner tension. In understanding this, rather than being angry, care-givers would probably be more sympathetic.

Again, it is important for the relative to understand that schizophrenic experiences of all kinds are real to the patient, not imaginary and not put on. It is useless to argue, to try to explain away their delusions, though relatives should firmly decline to act upon the patient's delusions. The relative has a right to set firm, if fairly tolerant limits to the patient's behaviour, while gauging the amount of pressure that can be brought upon him. The relative can gain some relief from the continual tension if the patient agrees to attend a day hospital, a day centre, or even to get a part-time job.

At the back of their minds relatives continue to question whether schizophrenia is curable. In answer, it must be pointed out again that 25% recover completely from an acute schizophrenic episode, even without medication. Another 65% improve significantly on medication, and many are able to return to their work, some to useful and near-normal lives. The aim of therapy should certainly be to restore gently the ability to earn a living and if possible to maintain a rightful place within the community.

A group of about 10% of schizophrenics, however, do remain totally disabled. They and others may need repeated admissions to hospital or may remain permanently in some hospital unit or its equivalent. Only a proportion of these needs to be permanently in hospital, but the management of the chronic patient is an issue that must be faced.

Community care

One of the burning issues at the moment is whether the demise of large mental hospitals is acceptable because so many patients will, of necessity, be transferred into the community. This theme has been aired in passing throughout these chapters, but the present situation should be summarised here because it has become so contentious. It is fallacious to argue exclusively for or against the closing of mental hospitals, since both hospital and community facilities are needed. As already stated, some patients (albeit a small group) will need permanent care in an institution or hospital. As emphasised, too, in-patient facilities are needed for those who relapse, and treatment should be given early rather than late. There will also be those with a poor prognosis but without major social handicaps who will need continuing care, especially when further relapses are likely, and prophylactic medication is necessary.

Meanwhile help may be needed to find suitable occupation, and care-givers need to spend time with any highly emotionally charged families. As described previously, community psychiatric nurses can undertake much of the treatment, and social workers can help with measures regarding housing and jobs.

Patients with chronic handicaps and poor social adjustment, as well as the behavioural defects characteristic of chronic schizophrenia, require more elaborate aftercare. This should include long-term plans for rehabilitation in the hospital *and* settlement outside hospital. Patients should also receive maintenance drug therapy, which should be closely supervised, as outlined in Chapter 4. Some handicapped patients will live more or less independently. Others will need sheltered work and accommodation.

The aim should be for the patient to live as normal a life as possible in the community, where appropriate. There must be sufficient resources in the community to ensure that the standards are at least equal to—if not better than—those of the mental hospitals. Sufficient in-patient beds should be available for assessment of those who do relapse and for those who need permanent care. Hospital and community facilities and settings are *both* needed, and the standards in both should be high and maintained so. To attain them, both undoubtedly need sufficient resources as well as goodwill towards the patients. Community care is not a cheap option but is effective when it has been planned properly, adequate resources supplied, and the staff involved trained to work in the new setting. Results across the country have been uneven; whereas some areas succeed, there are others where the deficiency in the service has only caused greater animosity and doubt.

When the patient persists in exhibiting abnormal behaviour, particular attention needs to be given to the problems of the family. Relatives may be helped by joining a voluntary group and meeting others who have had to deal with similar problems. Relatives' groups are useful, for they offer support, reduce isolation, and may enable relatives to observe and change some of their own more rigid or ineffective ways of dealing with the problems. Openness about particular difficulties may also lead to suggestions from other relatives of alternative ways of coping. There are in fact national self-help groups of relatives that provide viable support such as the National Schizophrenia Fellowship, the Schizophrenia Association of Great Britain, the Northern Schizophrenia Fellowship and the North-West Fellowship. (See Appendix B.)

When schizophrenia has obviously become chronic, a most detailed assessment is also needed. This should involve all those of the caring professions and the families and friends who have been supporting the patient, and is as necessary as the initial assessment when the patient first presented with possible schizophrenia. Attempts will be made to assess the type and severity of the mental illness and any physical disabilities, together with the assets and the residual strengths of personality and talents. The patient, carers and professional staff should then outline specific short- and long-term goals and delineate the strategies required to attain them. The specific tasks of the various members of staff should be outlined clearly, and progress should be monitored and evaluated regularly.

The obstacles to those goals must also be noted. These might well include the disabilities arising directly from the symptoms, especially negative ones such as apathy, lack of interest and drive; the social disadvantages of hostility in the home; and the lack of work, skills and educational attainment, with associated unemployment or even poverty.

Violence and compulsory detention for the schizophrenic

Relatives and other care-givers often complain of their fear of the disturbed, upsetting behaviour of the schizophrenic—understandably, since there has been a fundamental change in the personality and behaviour. Withdrawal and lack of communication are threats to a close relative, as is the opposite—over-activity. It must be stressed, however, that though often feared by laymen, major violence towards others is very uncommon. Homicide is rare. History of self-mutilation is however more frequent. About one schizophrenic in ten dies by suicide. In Philip's case there was a tragic, violent death, though the exact way he died and the circumstances surrounding it remain vague and clouded in mystery. Self-harm behaviours may well be associated with delusion of control or persecution, auditory hallucinations, or feelings of great despair and depression as the schizophrenic realises that he is snared by this dreadful illness.

Certainly the carers cannot cope with active suicidal or homicidal behaviour, so it is essential that patients be removed to a place of safety such as a hospital. Their general management is the same as for any other schizophrenic.

While medication is often needed to bring disturbed behaviour under immediate control, much can be done by providing a reassuring, calm, consistent environment in which provocation is avoided. Often a ward with an adequate number of experienced staff can be very effective. The intensive care ward in a hospital is invaluable. Unfortunately, during such a phase, the patient is most resistent and often does not agree to be admitted into hospital; or even if they do, they will demand to leave.

It is in these cases that a compulsory order under the appropriate section of the Mental Health Act (1983) must be used. As Mrs Moate's story shows clearly, a crisis now arises; it engenders great feelings of guilt in the relatives that they are colluding with the approved social worker and/or psychiatrist to force the patient to be taken from the home and admitted into a hospital or psychiatric unit.

Again, the patient often accuses the relative of having him 'put away', of rejecting him. Like so many others, Mrs Moate rued the day when she had to face such a decision. However, relatives are greatly helped in making up their minds if it is emphasised to them that 'to section' a patient is both a legal and a therapeutic act. It is a *legal* act in the fact that it is part of the law of Parliament, passed after due consideration of all the facts. Parliament came to the conclusion that there was a group of people who at some time in their lives needed to be compulsorily detained. At the same time, the Act emphasised that it was essential for certain conditions to be met: ie, the patient must be mentally ill and a danger to himself or others, and there could be no other way of dealing with the case.

Detainment is also a *therapeutic measure* in that it allows the patient to be treated in the best way, to receive the treatment which is most appropriate to him and his condition at that time. If he does not receive such treatment then disasters such as suicide or homicide can and do occur. Here again, the family should be consulted closely and their anxiety and guilt minimised.

Once the patient is in the hospital, restrictions are usually kept to the minimum required for safety and adequate treatment. Frequently, the patient and his family realise that compulsory hospital care is virtually the same as that for an informal patient, and no lasting harm is done to relationships between staff, patient and relatives. Other problems do occur, however, when patients are reluctant to be admitted and—as in the case of Philip—continually leave the hospital. In fact staff generally do remarkably well in dissuading informal patients who suddenly want to leave hospital not to do so, but there are times when they find it impossible to succeed.

In such conditions, when patients need effective treatment, a compulsory order must therefore be considered. The two most commonly used sections of the Act are Section Two (an admission for assessment for up to twenty-eight days) and Section Three (admission for treatment) which lasts for up to six months. Under Section Two, an approved social worker or the nearest relative makes an application; and two doctors, one who specialises in psychological medicine, have to recommend the admission. Under Section Three, the recommendation for admission must be made by two doctors and then an approved social worker or nearest relative must apply. The social worker must consult the nearest relative, unless this is not reasonably practical, or if such consultation would involve an unreasonable delay. If the relative does object, the social worker can make an application to the County Court to displace the nearest relative.

In the case of a dire emergency when there is 'urgent necessity' for the patient to be admitted, and when the course of normal procedures would involve 'undesirable delay', the admission, which lasts up to seventy-two hours (this time under Section Four), must be recommended by one doctor with an application being made by the approved social worker or nearest relative. Patients can oppose (in a mental health review tribunal) their compulsory detention, and the tribunal will then decide whether or not the compulsory order should remain in force.

The Mental Health Act (1983) has also brought in certain restrictions regarding treatment procedures. Some treatment categories cannot be given, without specific consent, to compulsorily detained patients. These include

1 Psychosurgery and sex hormone implant treatment and
2 ECT and medication *after* it has been administered for three months.

Clearly, then, applications and implications of the Mental Health Act are complex. Clearly, too, along with sensitive early care and careful management of admission and discharge, home and community care, they form an important part of the general management of the schizophrenic.

6

Hope

In Philip's case the schizophrenic illness did end in a violent death that was the beginning of yet more suffering for the family. Mrs Moate gives her account of the various stages of grief that she went through. She is open throughout about the feelings of guilt and failure until, in time, she works through these feelings. It becomes clear that her Christian faith was one of the major factors in bringing her through the storm. Throughout the account she had been a member of the Salvation Army, and the Army—as well as specific friends and supporters—was a great help throughout Philip's illness. These people were not going to fail them when Philip died, and they are obviously still there supporting. In spite of all the suffering that the schizophrenic illness had caused, death had brought even greater suffering.

The poignant words that follow reveal the mental anguish of a mother:

> I cradled his face between my hands. This was the darkest moment of my life. I felt the ultimate in human pain as the crushing realisation dawned on me that Philip had died. That his life was no more. Yes, it was true—it *had* happened.[1]

---

[1] Page 74.

She gives a glimpse at this time too, of the strength which had sustained her and her family throughout the illness.

While he had lived, while he had struggled against the illness which had devastated his mind, his very being, there was always a source of hope: hope that by some miracle he might one day be well again; a whole person, free to enjoy life to the full. Goodness knows, he had fought so hard to be free, and fought to the last.[1]

Thus they had *hope*. They kept hoping against hope that the devastation and deterioration of his mind might be stemmed and that he might be made whole. Now she naturally queried why he had ever lived and why he had suffered so, to end in a violent death at the early age of sixteen. But immediately it is noticeable that the hurt and anger are mingled with 'a sense of calm and peace'. It was good to read that at this time of great grief, friends, neighbours and relatives sustained the family with their cards and letters of condolence. She says, 'We were cushioned and borne along by the love and support of others.' [2]

This calm would have arisen from the belief that although Philip was dead he would rise again. She states, 'Philip's life had just begun in eternity.' Hers was the Christian belief that 'We move on to an inheritance, undefiled, incorruptible that fadeth not away.' She believed that there would be a day coming when, 'They will wipe every tear from their eyes. There will be no more death, or mourning, or crying, or pain, for the whole order of things has passed away.' She was convinced therefore that the family would meet Philip 'in the

---

[1] Page 74.
[2] Page 75 and following.

morning', and this faith would sustain her through all the stages of her grief and be the basis on which she, John, Iain and Carol were to face their future lives without Philip.

Such a crisis is almost always a testing time for faith. Their faith was not to fail them, and as the months went by it became clear that she and her husband were sustained and increasingly strengthened by their Christian beliefs. After great clouds and storms the sun does break through. It was striking how the theme of eternal life—'See you in the morning'—was to emerge time and again into their lives during this period. Mary Moate reminds us, however, that at this time human fellowship is also needed. Her feeling—that in spite of all the concern and care demonstrated, no-one truly understood or could share her feelings—is quite natural. Sadly people are reluctant to talk about what in reality are the greatest facts of life— death and grieving; and to erase talk of the dead one does not erase the memories and grief.

Classically, numbness gave way in her to acute awareness of Philip's death and then deep grief at the loss of a son. It was then she had to learn to come to terms with death. Here facing her was the question of whether Philip committed suicide or not. The true motivation could never really be assessed, but she was aware that he was a tragic, lonely and sad victim of his terrible illness, an illness which finally cost him his life. Now it was the haunting question of whether she could have done more for her son which caused her guilt and anguish. And, allied to these questions were her doubts about her Christian faith, in particular whether these beliefs that had for years sustained her would now sustain her during the greatest crisis of her life.

Mrs Moate had accepted God's will in her own life, for there had been repeated proof of the guiding hand of the God of Love. Had they not 'received' three children when there had been no hope? Had he not shown love and concern for each of them over the years? Her dilemma now was this: how could the same God of Love who had sustained them thus allow such an awful thing to happen to them? In particular she continued to be haunted by the thought of why, why this dreadful crippling illness of the mind was allowed to exist.

But this poignant story ends as one of hope because Mary and her family did live through it, and were sustained by their Christian beliefs. She focuses on a passage in the Psalms which became a reality in their lives: '... in the shadow of Thy wings will I make my refuge, until these calamities be overpast' (Psalm 57:1). Christian faith is nothing if it is not real and relevant to the great crises of life. Mrs Mary Moate shows clearly that Jesus' life on Earth has shown us the ultimate in human pain and suffering selflessly born for our sakes.

I would add more. Jesus identified with—that is, he knew from his own experience—that hurt and loss, depression and despair of the downcast, and upon his cross he made himself the target of the downcasts' hate and anger. By bearing this burden and yet loving us, his aggressors, Jesus enabled us to face the worst in ourselves and to be changed. Similarly, Jesus faced and endured the humiliation of the paranoid and the abandonment of the schizoid. He shared and still shares with each of us the worst of our suffering. Even so, in Christ we shall all be made alive.

This is the basis of Mary Moate's hope. This is every believer's hope. This infinitely painful story about schizophrenia, about love and death, is a moving piece of writing, but its beauty cannot equal the courage shown by Mary Moate herself in writing it. The story affects us so deeply, simply because she so clearly reveals the suffering of a son, the suffering of herself and of her family—but ultimately the coming through to glorious hope.

That we, the onlookers and sometimes care-givers, are

challenged on the way need not make us turn away or despair. Rather this book should make us all—professionals, carers, relatives, friends and Christians—look anew at our role of support and empathy. For society will be judged not on its economic success but on how it deals with the weak and the suffering in our midst. Even more, by that criterion we will be judged in eternity for 'As much as you do unto one of the least of these you do it unto me'. 'I was sick and you visited me' (Matthew 25). Jesus stands among us today with nail-prints in his hands; he reminds us that he died for them—the schizophrenics—just as he did for you and for me.

APPENDIX A

Glossary of Terms

Acute: (illness which is) rapid in onset and usually of a short duration.

Affect: feelings or emotions usually attached to ideas.

Affective disorders: the group of mental disorders with an emotional component, eg depression, mania.

Aggression: response aimed to injure or damage an object or person. It may be vocal, physical or symbolic.

Apathy: an attitude of indifference to an abnormal degree.

Autistic: preoccupied with one's own morbid thoughts and inner world, with an accompanying lack of communication, verbal and otherwise.

Ambivalence: the simultaneous existence of contrasting emotions such as love and hate towards the same person.

Anti-depressant: a drug used in the treatment of depressive illness and symptoms.

Anxiety: an emotional state characterised by apprehension, uncertainty and

141

unresolved fear. It can be a normal response to stress, but becomes morbid when excessive and unreasonable.

Behaviour: the total response of a person in a given situation.

Belief: a recognition or an acceptance of the truth and existence of something.

Blocking: the cutting off of an associated idea or thought due to mental conflict.

Catatonia: a state of profound mental withdrawal marked by an absence of voluntary motor activity.

Cognition: awareness of perception; knowing.

Coma: a state of unconsciousness so profound that the patient cannot be aroused.

Compulsion: performance of an act in response to an irresistible urge, though contrary to conscious inclination.

Confusion: a state of mind characterised by lack of clear thinking and disturbed orientation for time, place and/or person.

Delusion: a false belief impervious to reason, one that continues to be held in spite of overwhelming evidence to the contrary.

Dementia: progressive intellectual deterioration caused by a brain disease, eg, senile or pre-senile dementia.

Depression: a morbid state of sadness, dejection or melancholia associated with lowered mood levels and sleep disorder.

ECT: (Electro Convulsive Therapy) is a treatment in which an electric current is passed across the skull of an anaesthetised, relaxed patient. It is now limited to the treatment of severe depressive illnesses that do not respond to other forms of treatment such as anti-depressants.

EEG: (Electro Encephalography) is a recording of the electrical impulses generated by the nerve cells of the brain. An abnormal tracing can indicate epilepsy or a focal lesion, although the use of EEG is limited as a diagnostic aid.

Extrapyramidal signs: occur when there are disorders of a group of nuclei in the brain and central nerve cells involved in co-ordination of movement. These extrapyramidal effects can result from *neuroleptic* (major tranquillisers) medication. These extrapyramidal symptoms include:

Akathisia: motor restlessness, accompanied by a jittery or anxious feeling.

Akinesia: a paucity of movement associated with muscular fatigue or weakness and apparent apathy and inertia.

Dystonia: involuntary movements of abrupt onset; may include facial distortion and grimacing, *retrocollis* (drawing back of the head), *torticollis* (twisting of the neck), *dysarthria* (speech impairment).

Oculogyric crisis: an extreme form of dystonia (see above) in which the eyes remain fixed for a time and then move upwards and sideways, remaining in that position.

Tardive Dyskinesia: this is of late onset where the cheek, tongue and jaw movements are implicated, often resembling 'fly-catching' or 'lip smacking'.

Flattening of affect: emotional shallowness or lack of emotional response.

Grief: an emotion of profound sadness usually following loss of a key person.

Hallucination: an apparent false sensory perception in the absence of an adequate external stimulus. Any of the senses may be involved—auditory, olfactory, visual, tactile. The most frequently encountered in schizophrenia are auditory hallucinations.

Ideas of reference: ideas, beliefs quite unfounded that others are speaking about you—a feature of paranoia (see below).

Illusion: a false perception (a misinterpretation).

Incoherence: an absence of an orderly flow of ideas.

Innate: in-born or inherited.

Insight: awareness of a situation or one's own mental condition.

Intelligence: general all-round ability to perform mental tasks.

Introvert: one who tends to be introspective or inward looking.

Mania: disordered mental state of high, uncontrolled excitement often associated with excessive motor activity and ideas of grandeur.

Morbid: pathological; abnormal in quality, degree or duration.

Negativism: reduction in activity, indifference or resistance to suggestions or commands.

Neuroleptic: anti-psychotic drug (a major tranquilliser) used in the treatment of psychotic disorders to control the major symptoms, eg, hallucinations, delusions.

Neurosis: a group of mental disorders less pronounced than the psychoses, where insight is preserved and sense of reality maintained.

Orientation: ability to recognise and locate one's self in respect to time, place and other persons.

Panic: a sudden, overpowering feeling of terror.

Paranoia: a psychosis characterised by fixed and systematised delusions.

Paranoid: mental disorganisation characterised by delusions and/or hallucinations usually having to do with persecution.

Passive: characterised by inactivity; being submissive.

Pathogenic: giving rise to disease/disorder.

Pathognomonic: where certain features of a disease are specifically characteristic of that disease.

Phobia: an exaggerated and pathological fear of an object or situation.

Psychiatrist: a medically qualified person who

practices the speciality of psychological medicine.

Psychiatry: that branch of medicine which deals with mental illness/disorders.

Psychologist: a person not medically trained who is qualified in the study of psychology.

Psychology: the study of human and animal behaviour.

Psychopathology: the science which investigates the mental factors, influences and mechanisms underlying mental disorders.

Psychotherapy: psychological methods (especially listening and talking) of treatment of mental disorders.

Psychosis: a major mental illness in which there is disorganisation of the personality, where the patient suffers severe symptoms, lacks insight and is divorced from reality.

Functional psychosis: a psychosis with no apparent organic or physical basis, eg, schizophrenia.

Schizophrenia: a major psychosis characterised by thought disorder, delusions, hallucinations, unpredictable behaviour and apparent personality disintegration.

Somatic: pertaining to the body.

Syndrome: a group of associated symptoms.

Thought disorder: in general, where thinking is disordered in stream or content.

Trauma: a wound or injury, usually physical, but also mental, in the form of emotional shock.

Word salad: a mixed form of incomprehensible speech, containing nonsense words. Typical of schizophrenia.

APPENDIX B

Resources

Note: in no way does inclusion of these organisations necessarily imply CARE's endorsement of all their activities.

The National Schizophrenia Fellowship
78 Victoria Road
Surbiton, Surrey
KT6 4NS
Tel: 071-390 3651

This Fellowship is the largest support group in this country for schizophrenia and related problems. The NSF supports carers, relatives and sufferers; offers information and advice; campaigns through the media and in Parliament for better services, funding and research; organises conferences and meetings on schizophrenia and publishes many leaflets and reports.

The National Schizophrenia
Fellowship (Scotland)
40 Shandwick Place
Edinburgh
EH2 4RT
Tel: 031-226 2025

The Northern Schizophrenia
Fellowship
38 Collingwood Bldgs
Collingwood Street
Newcastle-upon-Tyne
NE1 1GH
Tel: 091-261 4343

The North-West
Schizophrenia Fellowship
46 Allen Street
Warrington
Cheshire
WA2 7JB
Tel: 0925 571680

The Southern Schizophrenia
Fellowship
17 Oxford Street
Southampton
Hants
SO1 1DJ
Tel: 0703 225664

The Midlands Schizophrenia
Fellowship
9 St Michael's Court
Victoria Street
West Bromwich
West Midlands
B70 8ET
Tel: 021-500 5988

The Northern Ireland
Schizophrenia Fellowship
47 Rosemary Street
Belfast
BT1 1QB
Tel: 0232 248006

SANE: Schizophrenia: A National Emergency
24 Oxford Street
London
W1A 5FE
Tel: 071-494 4840

Founded in 1986, SANE has drawn up an initial 'shopping
list' of twenty-six projects ranging from scientific research
into the causes of schizophrenia to practical help for its
sufferers and relief for their families.

The Schizophrenia Association of Great Britain
International Schizophrenia Centre
Bryn Hyfryd
The Crescent
Bangor, Gwynedd
LL57 2AG
Tel: 0248 354048

The SAGB aims to help patients suffering from mental illness, and their families; to promote research into the causes and symptoms of the disease; to educate the public about schizophrenia, and to enlist their support and sympathy.

MIND
(National Association for Mental Health)
22 Harley Street
London
W1N 2ED
Tel: 071-637 0741

MIND works in England and Wales for a better life for people diagnosed, labelled or treated as mentally ill. It does this through campaigning, community development training, publishing, and a comprehensive information service.

Northern MIND
158 Durham Road
Gateshead
Tyne & Wear NE8 4EL
Tel: 091-478 4425

North West MIND
21 Ribblesdale Place
Preston PR1 3NA
Tel: 0772 21734

South East MIND
4th Floor
24/32 Stephenson Way
London NW1 2HD
Tel: 071-380 1253

South West MIND
Bluecoat House
Saw Close
Bath BA1 1EY
Tel: 0255 64670

Trent and Yorkshire MIND
The White Building
Fitzalan Square
Sheffield
S1 2AY
Tel: 0742 21742

Wales MIND
23 St Mary's Street
Cardiff
CF1 2AA
Tel: 0222 395123

West Midlands MIND
Princess Chambers
(3rd Floor)
52/54 Lichfield Street
Wolverhampton
WV1 1DG
Tel: 0902 24404

Fellowship of Hope
42 Foxley Lane
Purley
Surrey
CR2 3EE

Prayer network and contact group with occasional meetings in London. Members seek to support and encourage each other by prayer and confidential newsletters of both information and testimony. No publicity or advertisements otherwise.

Association for the Pastoral Care of the Mentally Ill
39 St John's Lane
London
EC1M 4BJ
Tel: 071-253 9524

The APCMI offers a voluntary service of pastoral support to the mentally ill and their relatives by visiting and befriending. This is an interdenominational group with a Christian foundation offering help to anyone in need, whatever their creed, race or cultural background. ACPMI provides caring, listening, and training, and publishes a regular newsletter.

Royal College of Psychiatrists
17 Belgrave Square
London
SW1X 8PG
Tel: 071-235 2351/5

Founded in 1971, the College aims to advance the science and practice of psychiatry and related subjects; to further publication therein; and to promote study and research work in psychiatry.

Carers' National Association
29 Chilworth Mews
London
W2 3RG
Tel: 071-724 7776

Carers' National Association aims to encourage carers to recognise their own needs; to develop appropriate support for carers; to provide information and advice for carers, and to bring the needs of carers to the attention of government and other policy-makers.

Informal Caring Support Unit
King's Fund Centre
126 Albert Street
London
NW1 7NS
Tel: 071-267 4111

This programme aims to improve public recognition of informal carers and their contribution to care in the community; to increase the range and availability of information and training for informal carers and for professionals working with them.

The Hospital Chaplaincies' Council
Church House
Great Smith Street
London
SW1P 3NZ
Tel: 071-222 9011

The work of the Council is to watch (on behalf of the General Synod of the Church of England) matters affecting spiritual ministry in all medical institutions; to liaise between the Department of Health and Social Security and the Church of England; and to arrange appropriate training courses for appointed chaplains, clergy and laity. Pastoral care of the mentally ill is one of the many concerns of this Council.

The British Psychological Society
St Andrew's House
48 Princess Road East
Leicester
LE1 7BR

The British Psychological Society, founded in 1901, exists to promote the advancement of the study of psychology and its applications, and to maintain high standards of professional education and conduct. Meetings focus on the following areas of psychology: Psychotherapy, Educational, Occupational, Social, Mathematical, Statistical and Computing, Developmental, Cognitive, Counselling, Psychobiology, History and Philosophy, Health and Psychology of Women. The Society also has regional offices in Scotland, Northern Ireland and Wales.

A range of books published by the Society is available to members at reduced rates. The Society publishes seven journals and offers to members the services of a comprehensive collection of periodicals which are included as part of the

Psychology Library of the University of London, the Senate House, WC1E 7HU.

The Disabled Christians Fellowship
50 Clare Road
Kingswood
Bristol
BS15 1PJ
Tel: 0272 616141

This Fellowship seeks to promote Christian fellowship and to serve both the physically and mentally handicapped. It is an evangelical and interdenominational organisation based in Bristol but with local branches throughout the UK.

CARE
Christian Action, Research and Education
53 Romney Street, London, SW1P 3RF
Tel: 071 233 0455

The CARE mandate is:

To promote biblical and Christian action, research and education in order to support the integrity of the family, the centrality of marriage, and the sanctity of human life from conception.

To encourage those Christians already working in these fields, and to provide research and resource material to help them.

To assist every Christian throughout Britain to understand the moral issues facing society, and the role of the church in Christ-like caring.

To inspire and enable Christians to pray for this nation seeking God's forgiveness, power and direction for every aspect of our society.

To challenge Christians to be involved in the Parliamentary process both nationally and locally and to act as salt and light in areas where God's standards of righteousness, truth and justice need to be upheld.

To mobilise Christians in local practical caring initiatives to extend Christ's love within their own communities.

Caring For The Carers

by Christine Ledger

Caring means energy. It is not surprising, therefore, that long-term caring can become a physical and emotional assault-course for even the most compassionate person.

We can help those who look after others on a non-professional basis. Here some of them tell their own stories, before Christine Ledger—a carer herself both professionally and at home—goes on to suggest simple, realistic ways in which support and encouragement can be given to the unsung heroes of our society.

'An excellent, moving, practical, down-to-earth resource book for all those who are in the front line caring for family or friends, and for those who support them.'

DR PATRICK DIXON
Specialist in care of the dying and
Director, AIDS Care Education and Training

'A book that ought to be on every minister's shelves and in the home of any person who might one day find herself or himself at the point when caring passes into that area where they feel alone and forgotten.'
From the Foreword by **DR GEORGE CAREY**
Archbishop of Canterbury

This is part of a series of books published in association with CARE Trust, addressing the issues that call for political action and compassionate involvement and care.

Kingsway Publications

False Images

by Nigel Williams

'Pornography is a false image of the true nature of men and women as God created us. Let us celebrate the positive and campaign against the negative with all our might.'

Nigel Williams challenges the glamorous profile awarded to so much pornography today, and reveals the truth behind the images that attract so many, especially men.

Whether it is television or video, newspapers or magazines, or other media now being exploited by pornographers, you can do more than shake your head in dismay or disapproval. Here are practical steps that can be taken in the fight against pornography.

'Nigel Williams has powerfully strengthened the hands of those seeking to put more muscle into our legal controls on pornography.'

—MICHAEL ALISON MP

NIGEL WILLIAMS is Campaigns Director of CARE (Christian Action Research and Education).

This is part of a series of books published in association with CARE Trust, addressing the issues that call for political action and compassionate involvement and care.

Kingsway Publications